A2 Chemistry
UNIT 4

Edexcel

Unit 4: Periodicity, Quantitative Equilibria
and Functional Group Chemistry

George Facer

Philip Allan Updates
Market Place
Deddington
Oxfordshire
OX15 0SE

tel: 01869 338652
fax: 01869 337590
e-mail: sales@philipallan.co.uk
www.philipallan.co.uk

© Philip Allan Updates 2003

ISBN 0 86003 873 4

This guide has been written specifically to support students preparing for the Edexcel A2 Chemistry Unit 4 examination. The content has been neither approved nor endorsed by Edexcel/London Qualifications and remains the sole responsibility of the author. Exam questions are reproduced by permission of London Qualifications. London Qualifications accepts no responsibility whatsoever for the accuracy or method of working in the answers given.

Printed by Raithby, Lawrence & Co. Ltd, Leicester

Contents

Introduction

■ ■ ■

Content Guidance

■ ■ ■

Questions and Answers

Introduction

About this guide

This unit guide is one of a series covering the Edexcel specification for AS and A2 chemistry. It offers advice for the effective study of **Unit 4: Periodicity, Quantitative Equilibria and Functional Group Chemistry**. Its aim is to help you *understand* the chemistry — it is not intended as a shopping-list, enabling you to cram for an examination. The guide has three sections.

- **Introduction** — this provides guidance on study and revision, together with advice on approaches and techniques to ensure you answer the examination questions in the best way that you can.
- **Content Guidance** — this section is not intended to be a textbook. It offers guidelines on the main features of the content of Unit 4, together with particular advice on making study more productive.
- **Questions and Answers** — this shows you the sort of questions you can expect in the unit test. Answers are provided; in some cases, distinction is made between responses that might have been given by a grade-A candidate and those typical of a grade-C candidate. Careful consideration of these will improve your answers and, much more importantly, will improve your understanding of the chemistry involved.

The effective understanding of chemistry requires time. No-one suggests it is an easy subject, but even those who find it difficult can overcome their problems by the proper investment of time.

To understand the chemistry, you have to make links between the various topics. The subject is coherent; it is not a collection of discrete modules. These links only come with experience, which means time spent thinking about chemistry, working with it and solving chemical problems. Time produces fluency with the ideas. If you have that, together with good technique, the examination will look after itself.

The specification

The specification states the chemistry that can be used in the unit tests and describes the format of those tests. This is not necessarily the same as what teachers might choose to teach or what you might choose to learn.

The purpose of this book is to help you with Unit Test 4, but don't forget that what you are doing is learning *chemistry*. The specification can be obtained from Edexcel, either as a printed document or from the web at **www.edexcel.org.uk**.

The unit test

Command terms

Examiners use certain words that require you to respond in a specific way. You must distinguish between these terms and understand exactly what each requires you to do.

- **Define** — give a simple definition without any explanation
- **Identify** — give the name or formula of the substance
- **State** — no explanation is required (nor should you give one)
- **Deduce** — use the information supplied in the question to work out your answer
- **Suggest** — use your knowledge and understanding of similar substances or those with the same functional groups to work out the answer
- **Compare** — make a statement about *both* substances being compared
- **Explain** — use chemical theories or principles to say why a particular property is as it is
- **Predict** — say what you think will happen on the basis of the principles that you have learned

Calculations

You must show your working in order to score full marks. Be careful about significant figures. If a question does not specify the number of significant figures required, give your answer to *three significant figures* or to two decimal places for pH calculations.

Organic formulae

- **Structural formula** — you must give a structure that is unambiguous. For instance, $CH_3CH_2CH_2OH$ is acceptable, but C_3H_7OH could be either propan-1-ol or propan-2-ol and so is not acceptable. If a compound has a double bond, then it should be shown in the structural formula.
- **Full structural formula** — you must show all the *atoms* and all the *bonds*. 'Sticks' instead of hydrogen atoms will lose marks.
- **Shape** — if the molecule or ion is pyramidal, tetrahedral or octahedral you must make sure that your diagram looks three-dimensional. To do this, use wedges and dashes. Draw optical isomers as mirror images of each other. Geometric isomers must be drawn with bond angles of 120°. Make sure that the *bonds go to the correct atoms*, for example the oxygen in an –OH group or the carbon in $–CH_3$ and –COOH groups.

Points to watch

- **Stable** — if you use this word, you must qualify it. For example: 'stable to heat'; 'the reaction is thermodynamically stable'; 'the reaction is kinetically stable'; or 'a secondary carbocation intermediate is more stable than a primary carbocation'.

- **Reagents** — if you are asked to identify a reagent, you must give its *full* name or formula. Phrases such as 'acidified dichromate(VI)' will not score full marks. You must identify the acid used and give the reagent's full name, for example 'potassium dichromate(VI)'.
- **Conditions** — the word 'reflux' does not imply heating. If heat is needed, you must say so, i.e. 'heat under reflux'. Don't use abbreviations such as 'hur'.
- **Atoms, molecules and ions** — don't use these words randomly. Ionic compounds contain ions, not molecules.
- **Rules** — don't use rules such as Markovnikov or Le Chatelier to *explain*. However, they can be used to predict.
- **Melting and boiling** — when a molecular covalent substance (such as water) is melted or boiled, *covalent* bonds are *not* broken. So melting and boiling points are connected with the type and strength of *intermolecular* forces. When an ionic substance is melted, the ionic bonds are *not* broken — the substance is still ionic. The ions gain enough energy to separate.

Learning to learn

Learning is not instinctive — you have to develop suitable techniques to make good use of your time. In particular, chemistry has peculiar difficulties that need to be understood if your studies are to be effective from the start.

Planning

Busy people do not achieve what they do haphazardly. They plan — so that if they are working they mean to be working, and if they are watching television they have planned to do so. Planning is essential. You must know what you have to do each day and each week and set aside time to do it.

Be realistic in your planning. You cannot work all the time, so you must build in time for recreation and family responsibilities.

Targets

When devising your plan, have a target for each study period. This might be a particular section of the specification, or it might be rearranging of information from text into pictures, or the construction of a flowchart relating all the organic reactions you need to know. Whatever it is, be determined to master your target material before you leave it.

Reading chemistry textbooks

Chemistry textbooks are a valuable resource, not only for finding out the information for your homework but also to help you understand concepts of which you are unsure. They need to be read carefully, with a pen and paper to hand for jotting down things as you go — for example making notes, writing equations, doing calculations and drawing diagrams. Reading and revising are *active* processes which require concentration. Looking vaguely at the pages is a waste of time. In order to become fluent and confident in chemistry, you need to master detail.

Chemical equations

Equations are quantitative, concise and internationally understood.

When you write an equation, check that:

- you have thought of the *type* of reaction occurring — for example, is it neutralisation, addition or disproportionation?
- you have written the correct formulae for all the substances
- your equation balances both for the numbers of atoms of each element and for charge
- you have not written something silly, such as having a strong acid as a product when one of the reactants is an alkali
- you have included *state symbols* in all thermochemical equations and otherwise if they have been asked for

Graphs

Graphs give a lot of information, and they must be understood in detail rather than as a general impression. Take time over them. Note what the axes are, the units, the shape of the graph and what the shape means in chemical terms. Think about what could be calculated from the graph. Note if the graph flattens off and what that means. This is especially important in kinetics.

When drawing a graph, do not join up the points — draw a smooth line (straight or curved) as near as possible to all the points. However, if you are plotting a list, such as the first ionisation energies of the elements, then you do join up the points.

Tables

These are a means of displaying a lot of information. You need to be aware of the table headings and the units of numerical entries. Take time over them. What trends can be seen? How do these relate to chemical properties? Sometimes it can be useful to convert tables of data into graphs. Make sure that you use all the data when answering an examination question.

Diagrams

Diagrams of apparatus should be drawn in section. When you see them, copy them and ask yourself why the apparatus has the features it has. What is the difference between a distillation and a reflux apparatus, for example? When you do practical work, examine each piece of the apparatus closely so that you know both its form and function.

Calculations

Calculations are not normally structured in A2 as they were in AS. Therefore, you will need to *plan* the procedure for turning the data into an answer.

- Set your calculations out fully, making it clear what you are calculating at each step. Don't round figures up or down during a calculation. Either keep all the numbers on your calculator or write any intermediate answers to four significant figures.

- If you have time, check the accuracy of each step by recalculating it. It is so easy to enter a wrong number into your calculator or to calculate a molar mass incorrectly.
- Finally, check that you have the correct *units* in your answer and that you have given it to an appropriate number of *significant figures* — if in doubt, give it to three.

Notes

Most students keep notes of some sort. Notes can take many forms: they might be permanent or temporary; they might be lists, diagrams or flowcharts. You have to develop your own styles — note the plural. For example, notes that are largely words can often be recast into charts or pictures and this is useful for imprinting the material. The more you rework the material, the clearer it will become.

Whatever form your notes take, they must be organised. Notes that are not indexed or filed properly are useless, as are notes written at enormous length and those written so cryptically that they are unintelligible a month later.

Writing

There is some requirement for extended writing in Unit Test 4. You need to be able to write concisely and accurately. This requires you to marshal your thoughts properly and needs to be practised during your ordinary learning.

For experimental plans, it is a good idea to write your answer as a series of bullet points. There are no marks specifically for 'communication skills', but if you are not able to communicate your ideas clearly and accurately, you will not score full marks. The space available for an answer is a poor guide to the amount that you have to write — handwriting sizes differ hugely, as does the ability to write crisply. Filling the space does not necessarily mean you have answered the question. The mark allocation suggests the number of points to be made, not the amount of writing needed.

Approaching the unit test

The unit test is designed to allow you to show the examiner what you know. Answering questions successfully is not only a matter of knowing the chemistry but is also a matter of technique. Unit Test 4 is a paper with structured questions only, which are answered on the question paper.

Revision

- Start your revision in plenty of time. Make a list of what you need to do, emphasising the topics that you find most difficult — and draw up a detailed revision plan. Work back from the examination date, ideally leaving an entire week free from fresh revision before that date. Be realistic in your revision plan and then add 25% to the timings because everything takes longer than you think.

- When revising, make a note of difficulties and ask your teacher about them. If you do not make these notes you will forget to ask.
- Make use of past papers. Similar questions are regularly asked, so if you work through as many past papers and answers as possible, you will be in a strong position to obtain a top grade.
- When you use the Question and Answer section of this guide, make a determined effort to write *your* answers *before* looking at the sample answers and examiner's comments.

The exam

Unit Test 4 consists of a structured question paper of duration 1 hour 30 minutes, worth 75 marks. This counts for 30% of the A2 or 15% of the A-level marks.

This unit test examines the content of Unit 4 and some AS chemistry, especially organic. It also tests your exam technique!

- Read the question. Questions usually change from one examination to the next. A question that looks the same, at a cursory glance, to one that you have seen before usually has significant differences when read carefully. Needless to say, candidates do not receive credit for writing answers to their own questions.
- Be aware of the number of marks available for a question. This is an excellent pointer to the number of things you need to say.
- Do not repeat the question in your answer. We can all see the question. The danger is that you fill up the space available and think that you have answered the question, when in reality some or maybe all of the real points have been ignored.
- Look for words in **bold** in a question and make sure that you have answered the question fully in terms of those words or phrases. For example, if the question asks you to define a **dative covalent bond**, make sure that you explain the meaning of covalent bond as well as dative.
- Questions in Unit Test 4 will often involve substances or situations that are new to you. This is deliberate and is what makes these questions synoptic. Don't be put off by large organic molecules. They are nothing more than a collection of functional groups which, you may assume, react independently of each other.

Unit Test 4 has two assessment objectives:
- AO1 is 'knowledge with understanding' and makes up 40% of the test. You should be able to:
  - recognise, recall and show understanding of specific chemical facts, principles, concepts, practical techniques and terminology
  - draw on existing knowledge to show understanding of the responsible use of chemistry in society
  - select, organise and present information clearly and logically, using specialist vocabulary where appropriate

- AO2 is 'application of knowledge and understanding, analysis, synthesis and evaluation' and makes up 60% of Unit Test 4. You should be able to:
  - describe, explain and interpret phenomena and effects in terms of chemical principles and concepts
  - present arguments and ideas clearly and logically, using specialist vocabulary where appropriate
  - interpret and translate, from one form into another, data presented as continuous prose or in tables, diagrams and graphs
  - carry out calculations
  - apply chemical principles and concepts to unfamiliar situations, including those related to the responsible use of chemistry in society
  - assess the validity of chemical information, experiments, inferences and statements

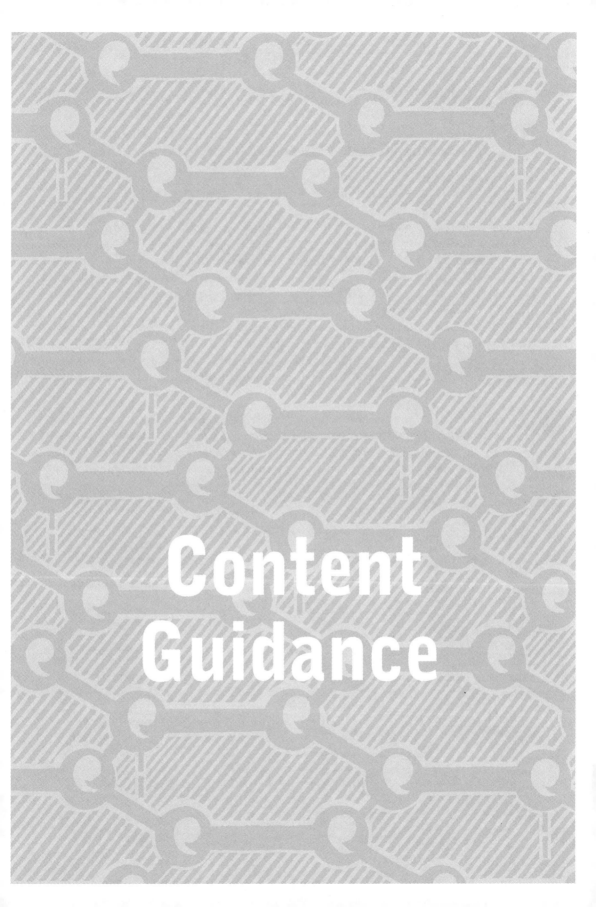

Content
Guidance

This section is a guide to the content of **Unit 4: Periodicity, Quantitative Equilibria and Functional Group Chemistry**. It does not constitute a textbook for Unit 4 material.

The main areas of this unit are:
- Energetics — Born–Haber cycles; lattice energy; hydration enthalpy; solubility of ionic substances
- Period 3 and group 4 — trends across period 3; reactions of period 3 elements with oxygen, chlorine and water; acid–base character of the oxides and metallic hydroxides; reactions of the chlorides with water; trends down group 4; behaviour of carbon and silicon tetrachlorides with water
- Chemical equilibria — defining and calculating K_c and K_p; factors affecting K and the equilibrium position
- Acid–base equilibria — Brønsted–Lowry theory; calculation of pH of weak and strong acids; acid–base tritrations; buffer solutions
- Organic chemistry — optical isomerism; Grignard reagents; carboxylic acids; acid chlorides; esters; carbonyl compounds; primary amines; nitriles; amides; amino acids

For each part of the specification, you should also consult a standard textbook for more information. Chemistry is a subtle subject, and you need to have a good sense of where the information you are dealing with fits into the larger chemical landscape. This only comes by reading. Remember that the specification tells you only what can be examined in the unit test.

Energetics

Required AS chemistry

Enthalpy change, ΔH

Enthalpy is a measure of chemical energy. When substances react, chemical energy is changed into heat (and other forms of energy, such as work). The enthalpy change is the heat change at constant pressure. If the reaction gives out heat (an **exothermic** reaction), enthalpy is lost and so the value of ΔH is negative. Therefore, the sign of ΔH indicates the direction of flow of heat.

Enthalpy changes are normally measured under standard conditions, which are:
- a constant pressure of 1 atmosphere
- a specified temperature, usually 298 K

Standard enthalpy of formation, ΔH_f

This is the heat change for the formation of one mole of substance from its *elements*, all substances being in their most stable states at 1 atm pressure and a specified temperature. For example, for ethanol it is the heat change per mole of ethanol for the reaction:

$$2C(s) + 3H_2(g) + \tfrac{1}{2}O_2(g) \longrightarrow C_2H_5OH(l)$$

Standard enthalpy of neutralisation, ΔH_{neut}

This is the heat change when an acid is neutralised by an alkali to produce one mole of water at 1 atm pressure and a specified temperature. For example, for sulphuric acid, it is the heat change per mole of water for the reaction:

$$\tfrac{1}{2}H_2SO_4(aq) + NaOH(aq) \longrightarrow \tfrac{1}{2}Na_2SO_4(aq) + H_2O(l)$$

Standard enthalpy of combustion, ΔH_c

This is the exothermic heat change when one mole of substance is completely burnt in excess oxygen, with all substances being in their most stable state at 1 atm pressure and a specified temperature. For example, for ethanol, it is the heat change per mole of ethanol for the reaction:

$$C_2H_5OH(l) + 3O_2(g) \longrightarrow 2CO_2(g) + 3H_2O(l)$$

Enthalpy level diagrams

These show the relative enthalpy levels of the reactants and the products:
- For an exothermic reaction, the enthalpy level of the reactants is *higher* than that of the products, and ΔH is negative.
- For an endothermic reaction, the enthalpy level of the reactants is *lower* than that of the products and ΔH is positive.

An exothermic reaction   **An endothermic reaction**

Enthalpy

Reactants

ΔH

Products

Enthalpy

Products

ΔH

Reactants

Tip In an enthalpy level diagram there is no need to draw in the activation energy, but for a reaction profile diagram it must be drawn.

Hess's law

Hess's law states that the enthalpy change for the process $A \longrightarrow B$ is independent of the route used to bring about that change. Hess's law cycles can be used to calculate enthalpy of reaction from, for example, enthalpies of formation.

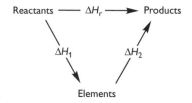

Reactants —— ΔH_r —→ Products

ΔH_1 ΔH_2

Elements

According to the law:

$\Delta H_r = \Delta H_1 + \Delta H_2$

where ΔH_1 = –(the sum of the enthalpies of formation of the reactants) and ΔH_2 = (the sum of the enthalpies of formation of the products). Thus

$\Delta H_r = \Sigma(\Delta H_{formation}$ of products) $- \Sigma(\Delta H_{formation}$ of reactants)

The enthalpy of reaction can also be calculated from enthalpy of combustion data.

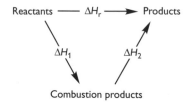

Reactants —— ΔH_r —→ Products

ΔH_1 ΔH_2

Combustion products

According to the law:

$\Delta H_r = \Delta H_1 + \Delta H_2$

where ΔH_1 = (the sum of the enthalpies of combustion of the reactants) and ΔH_2 = –(the sum of the enthalpies of combustion of the products).

A2 chemistry

Definitions

Enthalpy of atomisation, ΔH_a

This is the heat change when 1 mole of gaseous atoms is formed from the element in its most stable state at 1 atm pressure and a specified temperature.

Some atomisation reactions are given in the table below.

Element	Reaction
Sodium	$Na(s) \longrightarrow Na(g)$
Chlorine	$\frac{1}{2}Cl_2(g) \longrightarrow Cl(g)$
Phosphorus, P_4	$\frac{1}{4}P_4(s) \longrightarrow P(g)$
Sulphur, S_8	$\frac{1}{8}S_8(s) \longrightarrow S(g)$

Hydration enthalpy, ΔH_{hyd}

This is the heat change when 1 mole of gaseous ions is dissolved in excess water to form an infinitely dilute solution.

Some hydration reactions are given in the table below.

Ion	Reaction
Calcium	$Ca^{2+}(g) + aq \longrightarrow Ca^{2+}(aq)$
Hydroxide	$OH^-(g) + aq \longrightarrow OH^-(aq)$

Enthalpy of solution, ΔH_{soln}

This is the heat change when 1 mole of substance is dissolved in excess water. Using calcium hydroxide as an example, it is the heat change for the reaction:

$$Ca(OH)_2(s) + aq \longrightarrow Ca^{2+}(aq) + 2OH^-(aq)$$

Note: enthalpy of solution refers to *substances*, whereas hydration enthalpy refers to *ions*.

Lattice energy, *LE*

This is the *exothermic* heat change when 1 mole of ionic solid is formed from its gaseous ions. Using calcium hydroxide as an example, it is the heat change for the reaction:

$$Ca^{2+}(g) + 2OH^-(g) \longrightarrow Ca(OH)_2(s)$$

Born–Haber cycles

A Born–Haber cycle is a Hess's law cycle in which:
- the direct change is from elements to a solid ionic compound
- the indirect route involves atomising the elements, ionising the atoms and bringing the gaseous ions together to form the solid ionic compound

Tip Born–Haber cycles can be drawn as enthalpy level diagrams, but need not be in Edexcel A2 unit tests.

The cycle for lithium chloride is:

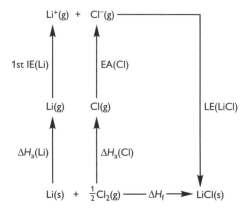

where 1st IE(Li) = first ionisation energy of lithium and EA(Cl) = electron affinity of chlorine.

$$\Delta H_f = \Delta H_a(Li) + 1st\ IE(Li) + \Delta H_a(Cl) + EA(Cl) + LE(LiCl)$$

The cycle for calcium chloride is:

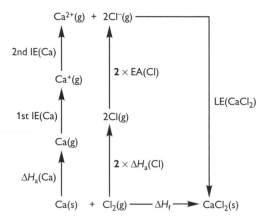

$$\Delta H_f = \Delta H_a(Ca) + 1st\ IE(Ca) + 2nd\ IE(Ca) + \mathbf{2}\Delta H_a(Cl) + \mathbf{2}EA(Cl) + LE(CaCl_2)$$

Note that:

- the second ionisation energy is for the process $M^+(g) \longrightarrow M^{2+}(g)$ and *not* for $M(g) \longrightarrow M^{2+}(g)$
- the energy change for the process $Cl_2(g) \longrightarrow 2Cl(g)$ is *twice* the enthalpy of atomisation of chlorine

Application of Born–Haber cycles

Born–Haber cycles can be used to determine the electron affinity of an atom or the lattice enthalpy of an ionic solid.

Worked example

Calculate the electron affinity for the F^- ion, given the following data.

	Enthalpy change/kJ mol^{-1}
ΔH_a of magnesium	+150
First ionisation energy of magnesium	+736
Second ionisation energy of magnesium	+1450
ΔH_a of fluorine	+79
Lattice energy of $MgF_2(s)$	−2900
ΔH_f of $MgF_2(s)$	−1102

Answer

The Born–Haber cycle is:

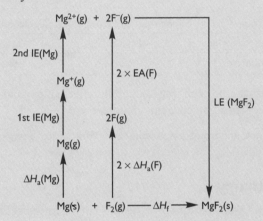

$$-1102 = +150 + 736 + 1450 + 2 \times (+79) + 2 \times EA(F) + (-2900)$$
$$2 \times EA(F) = -1102 - 150 - 736 - 1450 - 158 + 2900 = -696$$

$$\text{Electron affinity of fluorine} = \frac{-696}{2} = -348 \, \text{kJ mol}^{-1}$$

Lattice energy

Factors determining lattice energy

Ionic charge

The greater the charge, the stronger is the force between the positive and the negative ions. Therefore, the lattice energy is larger (more exothermic). For example, the lattice energy of magnesium fluoride (MgF_2), which contains the Mg^{2+} ion, is much larger (more exothermic) than that of sodium fluoride (NaF), which contains the Na^+ ion.

Sum of the ionic radii

The smaller the sum of the ionic radii, the stronger is the force between the positive and the negative ions. Therefore, the lattice energy is larger. For example:

- the lattice energy of sodium fluoride is larger than that of sodium chloride because the fluoride ion has a smaller radius than the chloride ion
- the lattice energies of the hydroxides or sulphates of group 2 decrease down the group as the cations get larger

Extent of covalency

The lattice energy also depends upon the extent to which the anion is polarised by the cation, which causes a slight degree of covalency. Large anions, such as I^-, are easily polarised. Small, highly charged cations, such as Mg^{2+} or Al^{3+}, are powerful polarising agents.

If a significant degree of polarisation occurs, the experimental lattice energy obtained from a Born–Haber cycle will be greater than that calculated from the purely ionic model. The experimental (Born–Haber) and calculated values for magnesium chloride and sodium fluoride are shown below.

Substance	Experimental/kJ mol^{-1}	Calculated/kJ mol^{-1}
Magnesium chloride	−2493	−2326
Sodium fluoride	−902	−901

From these values it can be seen that sodium fluoride is almost 100% ionic, whereas magnesium chloride has some covalent character.

Tip This factor is not important when comparing the lattice energies of two different compounds.

Hydration enthalpy

Hydration enthalpy is always exothermic, because of the forces of attraction involved:
- Cations are surrounded by the δ– oxygen atoms in water.
- Anions are surrounded by the δ+ hydrogen atoms in water.

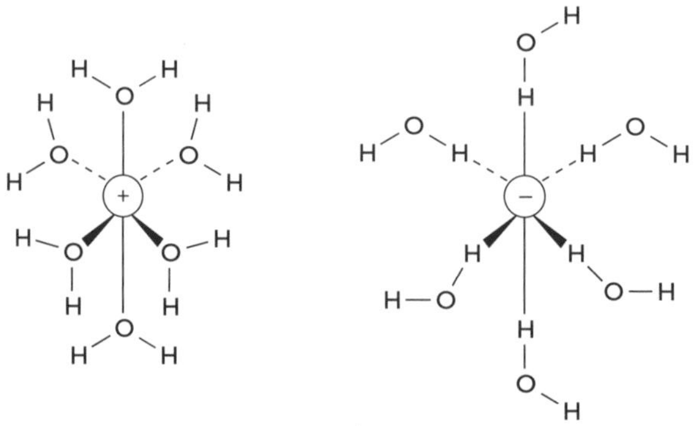

Factors determining hydration enthalpy
Ionic charge
The greater the charge, the stronger is the ion/dipole force of attraction between the

ion and the water molecules. Therefore, the hydration enthalpy is larger (more exothermic). For example, the hydration enthalpy of the magnesium ion, Mg^{2+}, is larger than that of the sodium ion, Na^+.

Ionic radius

The smaller the radius of the ion, the stronger is the ion/dipole force of attraction between the ion and the water molecules. Therefore, the hydration enthalpy is larger. For example:

- the hydration enthalpy of the fluoride ion, F^-, is larger than that of the chloride ion, Cl^-
- the hydration enthalpy of a group 2 cation decreases as the group is descended ($Be^{2+} > Mg^{2+} > Ca^{2+} > Sr^{2+} > Ba^{2+}$)

Solubility

A solute is soluble in a given solvent if the energy required to separate the solute particles is compensated for by the energy released in the attractions between the solute particles and the solvent molecules.

Water is a solvent for substances that form either ion/dipole interactions or hydrogen bonds with water molecules.

Enthalpy of solution of ionic substances

Water dissolves many ionic substances because the exothermic hydration enthalpies compensate for the endothermic breakdown of the lattice (minus the lattice energy). This can be shown by a Hess's law cycle.

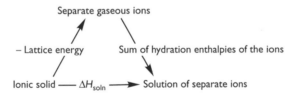

Thus,

ΔH_{soln} = −(lattice energy) + (the sum of the hydration enthalpies of the ions)

Worked example

Use the data in the table below to calculate the enthalpy of solution of magnesium chloride.

Enthalpy change	Value/kJ mol^{-1}
Lattice energy of magnesium chloride	−2493
Hydration enthalpy of $Mg^{2+}(g)$	−1920
Hydration enthalpy of $Cl^-(g)$	−364

Answer

The Hess's law cycle is:

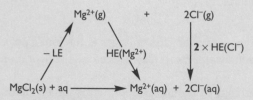

$$\Delta H_{soln}(MgCl_2) = -(\text{lattice energy}) + (\text{sum of hydration enthalpies of } Mg^{2+} \text{ and } 2Cl^-)$$
$$= -(-2493) + [-1920 + (2 \times -364)] = -155\,kJ\,mol^{-1}$$

Solubility of group 2 sulphates

- Solubility *decreases* down the group.

Compound	Solubility
Magnesium sulphate	Very soluble
Calcium sulphate	Slightly soluble
Strontium sulphate	Very slightly soluble
Barium sulphate	Insoluble

- The charge on the ions does not change.
- The radius of the cation *increases* as the group is descended. However, as the sulphate ion has a very large radius, the cation radius has little impact on the *sum* of the ionic radii. Therefore, the lattice energy only decreases slightly.
- The hydration enthalpy of the cation is independent of the anion and decreases markedly as the group is descended. The hydration enthalpy decreases more than the lattice energy and so ΔH_{soln} becomes less exothermic. This is why the solubility of the group 2 sulphates decreases down the group.

Soluble barium ions are poisonous. Insoluble barium sulphate is used as a 'barium meal' to investigate blockages in the digestive tract. Barium is opaque to X-rays and so by taking a series of images, the progress of barium sulphate through the gut can be followed. Insoluble barium carbonate cannot be used because it would react with the stomach acid to form soluble barium chloride, which is poisonous.

Solubility of group 2 hydroxides

- Solubility *increases* down the group.

Compound	Solubility
Magnesium hydroxide	Insoluble
Calcium hydroxide	Slightly soluble
Strontium hydroxide	Moderately soluble
Barium hydroxide	Soluble

- The charge on the ions does not change.
- The radius of the cation *increases* as the group is descended. The hydroxide ion has a radius similar to the group 2 cations, so the *sum* of the ionic radii increases significantly. This means that the lattice energy decreases markedly.
- The hydration enthalpy of the cation is independent of the anion and also decreases markedly as the group is descended. The lattice energy decreases slightly more than the hydration enthalpy, and so ΔH_{soln} becomes more exothermic. This is why the solubility of the group 2 hydroxides increases down the group.

Worked example

Use the hydration enthalpies and lattice energies below to explain why barium hydroxide is more soluble than strontium hydroxide.

	ΔH/kJ mol^{-1}
ΔH_{hyd} of Sr^{2+}	−1480
ΔH_{hyd} of Ba^{2+}	−1360
ΔH_{hyd} of OH$^-$	−460
Lattice energy of Sr(OH)$_2$	−1894
Lattice energy of Ba(OH)$_2$	−1768

Answer

ΔH_{soln} = −LE + (sum of hydration enthalpies of the ions)
ΔH_{soln} of Sr(OH)$_2$ = −(−1894) + [−1480 + (2 × −460)] = −506 kJ mol^{-1}
ΔH_{soln} of Ba(OH)$_2$ = −(−1768) + [−1360 + (2 × −460)] = −512 kJ mol^{-1}

ΔH_{soln} of barium hydroxide is more exothermic than ΔH_{soln} of strontium hydroxide. Therefore, barium hydroxide is more soluble.

Alternative answer

The lattice energy decreases by 126 kJ going from strontium hydroxide to barium hydroxide, but the hydration enthalpy decreases by only 120 kJ. As the lattice energy has to be overcome and the decrease in lattice energy is greater than the decrease in the exothermic hydration enthalpy, barium hydroxide is more soluble than strontium hydroxide.

Size match

Do not use the concept of 'size match' when explaining solubility. Anions are much bigger than cations that have the same number of electrons — compare Na$^+$ with F$^-$, both of which have the electronic configuration 2,8 (see the table overleaf).

A barium ion is much smaller than a sulphate ion and is similar in size to a hydroxide ion. However, barium sulphate is insoluble and the 'well-matched' barium hydroxide is soluble.

Cation	Radius/nm	Anion	Radius/nm
Mg^{2+}	0.065	OH^-	≈ 0.14
Ba^{2+}	0.135	SO_4^{2-}	≈ 0.62
Na^+	0.095	F^-	0.136
K^+	0.133	Cl^-	0.181

Period 3 and group 4

Introduction

The two major principles of the periodic table are that:
- going across a period, the elements become *less* metallic
- going down a group, the elements become *more* metallic

Properties characteristic of metals are that:
- they form lattices which consist of a regular arrangement of positive ions surrounded by a 'sea' of delocalised electrons
- they conduct electricity and are malleable
- they form cations such as Na^+, Mg^{2+} and Al^{3+}
- their oxides and hydroxides are basic and therefore react with acids to form salts

Properties characteristic of non-metals are that:
- they form either giant atomic lattices (in which the atoms are joined by strong covalent bonds throughout the lattice) or simple molecular lattices (in which the atoms within the molecule are joined by strong covalent bonds and the forces between the molecules are weak van der Waals forces)
- they do not conduct electricity and their solids are not malleable
- they form covalent bonds and those in groups 6 and 7 form anions such as S^{2-} and Cl^-
- they form oxo-anions, such as SiO_3^{2-}, PO_4^{3-}, SO_4^{2-} and ClO_3^-
- their oxides are acidic and so react with water to form acids or with bases to form salts

Note that graphite, a form of carbon (period 2), conducts electricity because of delocalised electrons in the plane of the interlocking hexagonal rings. However, it is not malleable and does not have any other properties of metals.

Amphoteric metals have some of the properties of both metals and non-metals. They form cations, but also oxo-anions and covalent bonds. Their oxides and hydroxides react with both acids and alkalis.

Note: this topic includes a large number of equations that *must* be learnt.

Period 3 (sodium to argon)

Trends across the period

Ionisation energy

The first ionisation energy increases across the period. The nuclear charge increases steadily without a significant increase in the shielding effect from the electrons. This means that the outer electrons are held more firmly. The pattern has two discontinuities.

- The first ionisation energy of aluminium is slightly less than that of magnesium because aluminium has a $3p$ electron at a slightly higher energy level, which is slightly easier to remove than a $3s$ electron in magnesium.
- There are four $3p$ electrons in sulphur, which means that two electrons are paired in a single orbital. These electrons repel each other so it is easier to remove one of the two paired electrons than an unpaired $3p$ electron in phosphorus.

Metallic character

Metallic character decreases across the period because as the ionisation energies increase, it becomes less energetically favourable to form cations.

- Sodium, magnesium and aluminium all form cations.
- Silicon and phosphorus form covalent bonds only.
- Sulphur and chlorine form anions and covalent bonds.
- Argon is a noble gas and does not form any compounds.

Oxidation number

There is a steady increase in the oxidation number across the period. However, phosphorus, sulphur and chlorine exhibit a range of oxidation states in compounds.

						+7
				+6	+5	
			+5	+4	+5	
		+4	+3	+4	+3	
	+3			+3		
+2				+2		
+1				+1	+1	
Na	**Mg**	**Al**	**Si**	**P**	**S**	**Cl**
					−2	−1

Oxides

The nature of the oxides changes from basic to amphoteric to acidic across the period.

- Sodium oxide (Na_2O) and magnesium oxide (MgO) are basic.
- Aluminium oxide (Al_2O_3) is amphoteric.
- Silicon dioxide (SiO_2), phosphorus oxide (P_4O_{10}), both sulphur oxides (SO_2 and SO_3) and chlorine monoxide (Cl_2O) are acidic.

Chlorides

The bonding in the chlorides changes from ionic to covalent across the period.

- Sodium chloride ($NaCl$) and magnesium chloride ($MgCl_2$) are ionic.
- Hydrated aluminium chloride ($[Al(H_2O)_6]Cl_3$) is ionic but anhydrous aluminium chloride ($AlCl_3$) is covalent.
- Silicon tetrachloride ($SiCl_4$), both phosphorus chlorides (PCl_3 and PCl_5), sulphur chloride (S_2Cl_2) and chlorine (Cl_2) are covalent.

Reactions of the elements

Reaction with oxygen

All the period 3 elements, except chlorine and argon, react to form oxides.

Sodium

On heating, sodium burns in oxygen with a yellow flame, forming sodium peroxide.

$$2Na + O_2 \longrightarrow Na_2O_2$$

At room temperature, sodium slowly oxidises to the simple oxide.

$$4Na + O_2 \longrightarrow 2Na_2O$$

To prevent oxidation, it is stored under oil.

Magnesium

Magnesium burns with a brilliant white flame, forming magnesium oxide.

$$2Mg + O_2 \longrightarrow 2MgO$$

Aluminium

Aluminium is protected from oxidation by a thin, protective layer of oxide. However, when strongly heated it burns, forming aluminium oxide.

$$4Al + 3O_2 \longrightarrow 2Al_2O_3$$

Silicon

On heating, silicon oxidises, forming silicon dioxide.

$$Si + O_2 \longrightarrow SiO_2$$

Phosphorus

Phosphorus burns when heated to just above room temperature.

$$P_4 + 5O_2 \longrightarrow P_4O_{10}$$

To prevent oxidation, phosphorus is stored under water.

Sulphur

Sulphur burns with a pale blue flame, forming sulphur dioxide.

$$S + O_2 \longrightarrow SO_2$$

Reaction with chlorine

All the period 3 elements, except chlorine and argon, react to form chlorides.

Sodium

On heating, sodium burns in chlorine forming the white, ionic solid, sodium chloride.

$$2Na + Cl_2 \longrightarrow 2NaCl$$

Magnesium

On heating in chlorine, magnesium reacts to form ionic magnesium chloride.

$$Mg + Cl_2 \longrightarrow MgCl_2$$

Aluminium

On heating in chlorine, aluminium reacts to form covalent, anhydrous aluminium chloride, $AlCl_3$.

$$2Al + 3Cl_2 \longrightarrow 2AlCl_3$$

When vaporised, $AlCl_3$ forms a dimer of formula Al_2Cl_6.

Silicon

Silicon reacts with chlorine to form the colourless, covalent liquid, silicon tetra-chloride.

$$Si + 2Cl_2 \longrightarrow SiCl_4$$

Phosphorus

In a limited supply of chlorine, phosphorus reacts at room temperature to form the colourless, covalent liquid, phosphorus trichloride.

$$2P + 3Cl_2 \longrightarrow 2PCl_3$$

With excess chlorine, the white, covalent solid, phosphorus pentachloride, is formed.

$$2P + 5Cl_2 \longrightarrow 2PCl_5$$

Tip Although, solid phosphorus has the formula P_4, it is often written as P in equations.

Sulphur

Molten sulphur reacts with chlorine to form covalent sulphur chloride, S_2Cl_2.

$$2S + Cl_2 \longrightarrow S_2Cl_2$$

Reaction with water

The period 3 metals react with water to give hydrogen, except for aluminium which is protected by a layer of oxide. The non-metals, except chlorine, do not react.

Sodium

Sodium reacts rapidly with water. It melts and buzzes around on the surface as it reacts, producing bubbles of hydrogen gas. A colourless, alkaline solution of sodium hydroxide is formed (pH $\approx$ 14).

$$2Na + 2H_2O \longrightarrow 2NaOH + H_2$$

Magnesium

Magnesium reacts slowly with cold water to form a suspension of magnesium hydroxide (pH $\approx$ 9) and hydrogen.

$$Mg + 2H_2O \longrightarrow Mg(OH)_2 + H_2$$

On heating in steam, magnesium burns with a brilliant white flame to form magnesium oxide and hydrogen.

$$Mg(s) + H_2O(g) \longrightarrow MgO(s) + H_2(g)$$

Aluminium, silicon, phosphorus and sulphur

None of these elements reacts with water.

Chlorine

Chlorine disproportionates reversibly in water to form two acids (pH $\approx$ 1).

$$Cl_2 + H_2O \rightleftharpoons HCl + HOCl$$

Acid–base character of oxides and metallic hydroxides

Principles

- Ionic oxides are basic because they contain the O^{2-} ion, which reacts with H^+ ions. Hence, metal oxides are bases. Metal oxides react with acids to form salts such as NaCl, $MgCl_2$ and $AlCl_3$.

- Covalent oxides react with water to form acids such as H_3PO_4, H_2SO_3, H_2SO_4 and HOCl. They react with alkalis to form salts such as Na_2SiO_3, Na_3PO_4, Na_2SO_3 or Na_2SO_4 and NaOCl. They do *not* react with acids.
- The high charge and small radius of the Al^{3+} ion make it highly polarising, causing the bond to the O^{2-} ion to become partially covalent. This means that Al_2O_3 has both metal oxide (ionic and basic) and non-metal oxide (covalent and acidic) properties. Both aluminium oxide and aluminium hydroxide react with acids *and* bases.

Reactions
Metal oxides and hydroxides are bases and so react with acids. Non-metal oxides are acidic and so react with bases. Aluminium oxide and hydroxide are amphoteric and so react with acids *and* strong alkalis.

Oxides and hydroxides of sodium and magnesium
The oxides and hydroxides in the table below are all bases. Sodium hydroxide is a soluble base and so is also an alkali. For each compound, molecular and ionic equations are given for a typical reaction with an acid.

Compound	Formula	Molecular and ionic equations
Sodium oxide	Na_2O	$Na_2O + H_2SO_4 \longrightarrow Na_2SO_4 + H_2O$ $Na_2O(s) + 2H^+(aq) \longrightarrow 2Na^+(aq) + H_2O(l)$
Sodium hydroxide	NaOH	$2NaOH + H_2SO_4 \longrightarrow Na_2SO_4 + 2H_2O$ $OH^-(aq) + H^+(aq) \longrightarrow H_2O(l)$
Magnesium oxide	MgO	$MgO + 2HCl \longrightarrow MgCl_2 + H_2O$ $MgO(s) + 2H^+(aq) \longrightarrow Mg^{2+}(aq) + H_2O(l)$
Magnesium hydroxide	$Mg(OH)_2$	$Mg(OH)_2 + 2HCl \longrightarrow MgCl_2 + 2H_2O$ $Mg(OH)_2(s) + 2H^+(aq) \longrightarrow Mg^{2+}(aq) + 2H_2O(l)$

Aluminium oxide, Al_2O_3
Aluminium oxide is **amphoteric**. It reacts with acids ($H^+(aq)$) *and* bases ($OH^-(aq)$).
$$Al_2O_3(s) + 6H^+(aq) \longrightarrow 2Al^{3+}(aq) + 3H_2O(l)$$
$$Al_2O_3(s) + 6OH^-(aq) + 3H_2O(l) \longrightarrow 2[Al(OH)_6]^{3-}(aq)$$

Aluminium hydroxide, $Al(OH)_3$
Aluminium hydroxide is also amphoteric. It reacts with acids ($H^+(aq)$) *and* bases ($OH^-(aq)$).
$$Al(OH)_3(s) + 3H^+(aq) \longrightarrow Al^{3+}(aq) + 3H_2O(l)$$
$$Al(OH)_3(s) + 3OH^-(aq) \longrightarrow [Al(OH)_6]^{3-}(aq)$$

If aqueous sodium hydroxide is added to a solution of an aluminium salt which contains $[Al(H_2O)_6]^{3+}(aq)$ ions, a white precipitate of hydrated aluminium hydroxide, $[Al(OH)_3(H_2O)_3]$, is obtained which then reacts with excess sodium hydroxide to form a colourless solution of sodium aluminate, $Na_3[Al(OH)_6]$.

Silicon dioxide, SiO_2
Silicon dioxide is weakly acidic. Solid silicon dioxide is a giant atomic lattice that is unreactive. Hot, concentrated aqueous sodium hydroxide reacts slightly with silicon

dioxide, but molten sodium hydroxide is required for complete reaction.

$$SiO_2(s) + 2NaOH(l) \longrightarrow Na_2SiO_3(l) + H_2O(g)$$

Phosphorus(V) oxide, P_4O_{10}

Phosphorus(V) oxide is strongly acidic. It reacts with water to form an acid that completely dissociates into $H^+(aq)$ ions and $H_2PO_4^-(aq)$ ions (pH ≈ 1).

$$P_4O_{10} + 6H_2O \longrightarrow 4H_3PO_4 \longrightarrow 4H^+ + 4H_2PO_4^-$$

Reaction with an aqueous alkali such as sodium hydroxide results in the formation of the salt sodium phosphate.

$$P_4O_{10} + 12NaOH \longrightarrow 4Na_3PO_4 + 6H_2O$$

Sulphur dioxide, SO_2

Sulphur dioxide is weakly acidic. It reacts with water to form sulphurous acid, H_2SO_3.

$$SO_2 + H_2O \longrightarrow H_2SO_3 \rightleftharpoons H^+ + HSO_3^-$$

Sulphurous acid is a weak acid (pH ≈ 2).

With aqueous sodium hydroxide, the salt sodium sulphite (also called sodium sulphate(IV)) is formed.

$$SO_2 + 2NaOH \longrightarrow Na_2SO_3 + H_2O$$

Sulphur trioxide, SO_3

Sulphur trioxide is strongly acidic. It reacts with water to form sulphuric acid, H_2SO_4.

$$SO_3 + H_2O \longrightarrow H_2SO_4 \longrightarrow H^+ + HSO_4^-$$

Sulphuric acid is a strong acid. It completely ionises into $H^+(aq)$ and $HSO_4^-(aq)$ ions (pH ≈ 1).

With aqueous sodium hydroxide, the salt sodium sulphate is formed.

$$SO_3 + 2NaOH \longrightarrow Na_2SO_4 + H_2O$$

Chlorine monoxide, Cl_2O

Chlorine monoxide is weakly acidic. It reacts with water to form chloric(I) acid (pH ≈ 4).

$$Cl_2O + H_2O \longrightarrow 2HOCl \rightleftharpoons 2H^+ + OCl^-$$

With aqueous sodium hydroxide, sodium chlorate(I) is formed.

$$Cl_2O + 2NaOH \longrightarrow 2NaOCl + H_2O$$

This disproportionates on heating to form sodium chloride and sodium chlorate(V).

$$3NaOCl \longrightarrow 2NaCl + NaClO_3$$

Reactions of the chlorides with water

Principles

- Ionic chlorides dissolve in water to form hydrated metal cations and chloride anions. If the charge density of the cation is high enough, the hydrated ion is deprotonated and the solution becomes acidic.
- Covalent chlorides react with water to form hydrochloric acid and either the non-metal oxide or one of its oxo-acids.

Reactions

Sodium chloride, NaCl

Sodium chloride is an ionic solid. It dissolves in water, forming hydrated ions.

$$NaCl(s) + aq \longrightarrow Na^+(aq) + Cl^-(aq)$$

The ions are not deprotonated, so the solution is neutral (pH = 7).

Magnesium chloride, MgCl$_2$

Magnesium chloride is an ionic solid. It dissolves in water, forming hydrated ions.

$$MgCl_2(s) + aq \longrightarrow Mg^{2+}(aq) + 2Cl^-(aq)$$

The $Mg^{2+}(aq)$ ion is really $[Mg(H_2O)_6]^{2+}(aq)$, which is slightly deprotonated by water.

$$[Mg(H_2O)_6]^{2+}(aq) + H_2O(l) \rightleftharpoons [Mg(H_2O)_5(OH)]^+(aq) + H_3O^+(aq)$$

This makes the solution *slightly* acidic (pH ≈ 5).

Hydrated aluminium chloride, [Al(H$_2$O)$_6$]Cl$_3$

Hydrated aluminium chloride is an ionic solid that dissolves in water. However, the high charge density on the small Al^{3+} ion causes the hydrated ion to be considerably deprotonated by water, forming an acidic solution (pH ≈ 3).

$$[Al(H_2O)_6]^{3+}(aq) + H_2O(l) \rightleftharpoons [Al(H_2O)_5(OH)]^{2+}(aq) + H_3O^+(aq)$$

Anhydrous aluminium chloride, AlCl$_3$

Anhydrous aluminium chloride is a covalent solid. It reacts with a limited amount of water, forming aluminium oxide and fumes of hydrogen chloride.

$$2AlCl_3 + 3H_2O \longrightarrow Al_2O_3 + 6HCl$$

With excess water, a solution of hydrochloric acid is formed (pH ≈ 1).

Silicon tetrachloride, SiCl$_4$

Silicon tetrachloride is a covalent liquid. It reacts rapidly with water, forming silicon dioxide and a solution of hydrochloric acid (pH ≈ 1).

$$SiCl_4 + 2H_2O \longrightarrow SiO_2 + 4HCl$$

Phosphorus(III) chloride, PCl$_3$

Phosphorus(III) chloride is a covalent liquid. It reacts with water, forming a solution of phosphorus(III) acid and hydrochloric acid (pH ≈ 1).

$$PCl_3 + 3H_2O \longrightarrow H_3PO_3 + 3HCl$$

Phosphorus(V) chloride, PCl$_5$

Phosphorus(V) chloride is a covalent solid. It reacts with water, forming a solution of phosphorus(V) acid and hydrochloric acid (pH ≈ 1).

$$PCl_5 + 4H_2O \longrightarrow H_3PO_4 + 5HCl$$

Sulphur chloride, S$_2$Cl$_2$

Sulphur chloride is a covalent orange liquid with a revolting smell. It reacts with water, forming a precipitate of sulphur in a solution of sulphurous and hydrochloric acids (pH ≈ 1).

$$2S_2Cl_2 + 3H_2O \longrightarrow 3S + H_2SO_3 + 4HCl$$

Group 4 (carbon to lead)

Trends down the group

Principles

- As the group is descended, the first ionisation energy decreases. Therefore, the elements become *more* metallic.
- As the group is descended, the +2 oxidation state increases in stability relative to the +4 state. This is because, as the ionic radius increases, the extra energy required to remove four electrons is not compensated for by the extra hydration or lattice energy.

Metallic character

The following properties illustrate the increase in metallic character of the elements as group 4 is descended.

Physical properties

Carbon exists as diamond and graphite. Diamond has a giant atomic structure in which each carbon atom is joined covalently to four other carbon atoms. It has a very high melting point, does not conduct electricity and is not malleable.

Graphite has a giant atomic structure in which each carbon atom is joined to three others in a plane, with the fourth bonding electron delocalised above and below the plane. It has a very high melting point, conducts electricity but is not malleable.

Silicon has a giant atomic structure similar to that of diamond. It has a high melting point, does not conduct electricity and is not malleable. When 'doped' by small quantities of some group 3 or group 5 elements, it becomes a semi-conductor.

Germanium has properties similar to those of silicon.

Tin has a metallic lattice structure, with a regular arrangement of tin ions surrounded by a 'sea' of delocalised electrons. It has a fairly low melting point (232 °C), conducts electricity and is malleable.

Lead has a metallic lattice structure. It has a fairly low melting point (327 °C), conducts electricity and is very malleable.

Note: a mixture of tin and lead melts at temperatures below 200 °C and is used as solder for electrical connections. However, the EU is banning its use because lead is poisonous.

Bonding

- Carbon, silicon and germanium form covalent bonds and oxo-anions.
- Tin and lead form the cations Sn^{2+} and Pb^{2+} respectively.

Acid–base character of the oxides

As the group is descended, the oxides become more basic.
- CO_2, SiO_2 and GeO_2 are acidic.
- SnO_2 is acidic; SnO is amphoteric.
- PbO and PbO_2 are amphoteric.

These properties are illustrated by the following reactions.

- Carbon dioxide reacts reversibly with water, forming carbonic acid.
  $$CO_2 + H_2O \rightleftharpoons H_2CO_3$$
  Carbonic acid is a weak acid.
- Carbon dioxide reacts with aqueous sodium hydroxide, forming the salt sodium carbonate.
  $$CO_2 + 2NaOH \longrightarrow Na_2CO_3 + H_2O$$
- Silicon dioxide reacts slowly with concentrated sodium hydroxide, forming sodium silicate.
  $$SiO_2 + 2NaOH \longrightarrow Na_2SiO_3 + H_2O$$
- Tin(II) oxide reacts with acids, forming Sn^{2+} ions, *and* with bases, forming $[Sn(OH)_4]^{2-}$ ions.
- Tin(IV) oxide reacts with concentrated sodium hydroxide to form $[Sn(OH)_6]^{2-}$ ions.

Tip You do not need to know the equations for the reactions of tin oxides.

- Lead(II) oxide reacts with acids to form Pb^{2+} ions.
  $$PbO(s) + 2H^+(aq) \longrightarrow Pb^{2+}(aq) + H_2O(l)$$
  It reacts with bases to form $[Pb(OH)_4]^{2-}$ ions.
  $$PbO(s) + 2OH^-(aq) + H_2O(l) \longrightarrow [Pb(OH)_4]^{2-}(aq)$$
- Lead(IV) oxide reacts with concentrated hydrochloric acid, to form $PbCl_4$.
  $$PbO_2 + 4HCl \longrightarrow PbCl_4 + 2H_2O$$
  It reacts with bases, forming $[Pb(OH)_6]^{2-}$ ions.
  $$PbO_2(s) + 2OH^-(aq) + 2H_2O(l) \longrightarrow [Pb(OH)_6]^{2-}(aq)$$

Relative stability of the +2 state

The +2 oxidation state increases in stability relative to the +4 state as the group is descended.

Tin

The +2 oxidation state in tin is *less* stable than the +4 state. This is demonstrated by the fact that Sn^{2+} ions are powerful reducing agents and are oxidised by chlorine or iodine to Sn^{4+} ions. For example:
$$Sn^{2+} + I_2 \longrightarrow Sn^{4+} + 2I^-$$

Tin(II) chloride will also reduce lead(IV) to lead(II).
$$SnCl_2 + PbCl_4 \longrightarrow SnCl_4 + PbCl_2$$

Lead

The +2 oxidation state is *more* stable than the +4 state. This is illustrated by the fact that lead(IV) oxide oxidises concentrated hydrochloric acid to chlorine.
$$PbO_2 + 4HCl \longrightarrow PbCl_2 + Cl_2 + 2H_2O$$

Also, on gentle heating, lead(IV) chloride decomposes to lead(II) chloride and chlorine.
$$PbCl_4 \longrightarrow PbCl_2 + Cl_2$$

Carbon and silicon tetrachlorides

In both CCl_4 and $SiCl_4$, the central atoms have four bonding pairs of electrons and no lone pairs. The four bonding pairs repel each other to a position of maximum separation, so both molecules are tetrahedral.

There are three important differences between the two molecules.

- The silicon atom in $SiCl_4$ has empty $3d$ orbitals that are at a similar energy level to the bonding electrons. Carbon has no $2d$ orbitals and so has no empty orbitals of similar energy.
- The radius of a carbon atom is smaller than the radius of the chlorine atom. Silicon is a much bigger atom, of similar size to the chlorine atom.
- Silicon tetrachloride is rapidly hydrolysed by water, whereas carbon tetrachloride does not react at all.

The reaction of water with silicon tetrachloride has the following mechanism.

- The lone pair of electrons on the oxygen atom in a water molecule forms a dative covalent bond into an empty $3d$ orbital in the silicon atom.
- The energy released by this bond-making is sufficient to break one of the silicon–chlorine σ-bonds.
- The process is repeated until all the chlorine atoms have been removed.

This mechanism is not possible with carbon tetrachloride because carbon does not have a $2d$ orbital (or any other empty orbital) at the required energy level. Therefore, the lone pair on an oxygen atom cannot form a dative covalent bond with the central carbon atom.

A second factor is that the carbon is completely surrounded by chlorine atoms. The oxygen atom in a water molecule cannot get close enough to attack the carbon atom — it is sterically hindered from attacking.

Tip Do not say that silicon tetrachloride has empty $3d$ orbitals. It is the central silicon atom that does.

Chemical equilibria
Required AS chemistry

Equilibrium

At equilibrium, the rate of the forward reaction equals the rate of the reverse reaction. When this state is reached, there is no further change in the concentrations of any of the substances involved.

Factors affecting equilibrium
Temperature
An increase in temperature moves the position of equilibrium in the endothermic direction.

Consider the reaction:

$$N_2(g) + 3H_2(g) \rightleftharpoons 2NH_3(g) \quad \Delta H = -92.4 \text{ kJ mol}^{-1}$$

An increase in temperature moves the position of equilibrium to the left.

Pressure

An increase in pressure moves the position of equilibrium towards the side with fewer gas moles. In the example above, high pressure moves the equilibrium position to the right, because there are two gas moles on the right compared with four on the left.

Concentration

If the concentration of a reactant is increased, the position of equilibrium moves towards the opposite side.

Consider the reaction:

$$2CrO_4^{2-}(aq) + 2H^+(aq) \rightleftharpoons Cr_2O_7^{2-}(aq) + H_2O$$

If the concentration of H^+ is increased, the equilibrium position shifts to the right. The colour changes from yellow (CrO_4^{2-} ions) to orange ($Cr_2O_7^{2-}$ ions).

Catalyst

A catalyst has *no* effect on the *position* of equilibrium. However, equilibrium is reached more quickly in the presence of a catalyst.

A2 chemistry

Definitions

Concentration

The **concentration** of a substance is defined as the number of moles in 1 dm^3 of solution. The symbol [A] means the concentration of substance A. The units are mol dm^{-3}.

Partial pressure

Partial pressure refers to gases. It is defined as the pressure that the gas would exert if it were alone in the vessel at the same temperature. It is calculated using the formula:

partial pressure = mole fraction × total pressure

$$\text{where mole fraction} = \frac{\text{the number of moles of that gas}}{\text{the total number of gas moles}}$$

Air contains 21% oxygen by moles, so the mole fraction of oxygen is 0.21. The partial pressure of oxygen in air at 2 atm = 0.21 × 2 = 0.42 atm.

Equilibrium constant, K

The equilibrium constant is a measure of the extent to which a reversible reaction takes place at a given temperature. A large value for the equilibrium constant means that a reaction is almost complete. A value greater than 1 means that the reaction proceeds further from left to right than from right to left.

The equilibrium constant can be measured:
- in terms of concentrations (K_c)
- for gases, in terms of partial pressures (K_p)

Expression for K_c

For a **homogeneous** equilibrium, the value of K_c is determined from the *equilibrium* concentrations of all the reactants and products. (Homogeneous means that all the reactants and products are in the same phase, for instance all gases or all in solution.)

For the reaction:

$$xA + yB \rightleftharpoons mC + nD$$

where x, y, m and n are the stoichiometric amounts in the equation, the value of K_c at $T°C$ is given by:

$$K_c = \frac{[C]_{eq}^m [D]_{eq}^n}{[A]_{eq}^x [B]_{eq}^y}$$

- $[C]_{eq}^m$ is the concentration of C at equilibrium raised to the power m.
- The temperature should *always* be quoted, because the value of an equilibrium constant varies with temperature.
- The units of K_c can be determined from the expression by cancelling out the units for the separate concentration terms.
- The expression for K_c is only valid when *equilibrium concentrations* are used.
- The quotient $\dfrac{[C]^m[D]^n}{[A]^x[B]^y}$ only equals K_c when the system is at equilibrium.

Worked example 1

State the expression for K_c and give its units for the reaction:

$$Br_2(aq) + 2Fe^{2+}(aq) \rightleftharpoons 2Br^-(aq) + 2Fe^{3+}(aq)$$

Answer

$$K_c = \frac{[Br^-]_{eq}^2 [Fe^{3+}]_{eq}^2}{[Br_2]_{eq} [Fe^{2+}]_{eq}^2}$$

The units are:

$$\frac{(\text{mol dm}^{-3})^2 \times (\text{mol dm}^{-3})^2}{(\text{mol dm}^{-3}) \times (\text{mol dm}^{-3})^2} = \frac{(\text{mol dm}^{-3})^4}{(\text{mol dm}^{-3})^3} = \text{mol dm}^{-3}$$

Worked example 2

Consider the reaction:

$$2SO_2(g) + O_2(g) \rightleftharpoons 2SO_3(g) \qquad K_c = 1.7 \times 10^6 \text{ mol}^{-1} \text{dm}^3 \text{ at } 700 \text{ K}$$

A steel vessel, volume 2 dm³, contains 0.2 mol SO_3, 0.04 mol SO_2 and 0.01 mol O_2. Show whether or not this mixture is at equilibrium. If not, indicate which direction the system will move in order to achieve equilibrium at 700 K.

Answer

$$K_c = \frac{[SO_3]^2_{eq}}{[SO_2]^2_{eq}[O_2]_{eq}} = 1.7 \times 10^6 \, mol^{-1} \, dm^3$$

$$[SO_3] = \frac{0.2}{2} = 0.1 \, mol \, dm^{-3}$$

$$[SO_2] = \frac{0.04}{2} = 0.02 \, mol \, dm^{-3}$$

$$[O_2] = \frac{0.01}{2} = 0.005 \, mol \, dm^{-3}$$

The quotient $= \dfrac{[SO_3]^2}{[SO_2]^2[O_2]}$

$$= \frac{0.1^2}{0.02^2 \times 0.005} = 5.0 \times 10^3 \, mol^{-1} \, dm^3$$

This value does not equal K_c. Therefore, the system is *not* at equilibrium.

The quotient is *less* than K_c. Therefore, its value must increase to achieve equilibrium. This means that the reaction will move to the right, increasing the concentration of SO_3 and decreasing the concentrations of SO_2 and O_2, until the value of the quotient equals 1.7×10^6. The system is then in equilibrium.

Calculation of K_c

In K_c calculations, you are always given the chemical equation plus some data. These data could be concentrations at equilibrium, in which case all you have to do is to put the values into the expression for K_c. However, you are usually given the *initial* amounts and either the amount of one substance at equilibrium or the percentage of a reactant converted. You *must* use equilibrium concentrations, *not* initial concentrations, in your calculation.

The calculation should be carried out in five steps.
- Step 1 — use the chemical equation to write the expression for K_c.
- Step 2 — construct a table and write in the initial number of moles of each substance.
- Step 3 — write in the table the change in moles of each substance and hence work out the number of moles at equilibrium.
- Step 4 — divide the equilibrium number of moles by the volume to get the concentration in $mol \, dm^{-3}$.
- Step 5 — substitute the *equilibrium* concentrations into the expression for K_c, and work out its value. At the same time, work out the units of K_c and include them in your answer.

Worked example

Phosphorus pentachloride, PCl_5, decomposes according to the equation:

$$PCl_5(g) \rightleftharpoons PCl_3(g) + Cl_2(g)$$

1.0 mol of phosphorus pentachloride was added to a $20\,dm^3$ flask and heated to 180 °C. When equilibrium had been established, it was found that 32% of the phosphorus pentachloride had decomposed. Calculate the value of K_c at 180 °C.

Answer

Step 1:

$$K_c = \frac{[PCl_3]_{eq}[Cl_2]_{eq}}{[PCl_5]_{eq}}$$

		PCl_5	PCl_3	Cl_2	Units
Step 2	Initial amount	1.0	0	0	mol
	Change	−0.32	+0.32	+0.32	mol
Step 3	Moles at equilibrium	1.0 − 0.32 = 0.68	+0.32	+0.32	mol
Step 4	Concentration at equilibrium	$\frac{0.68}{20} = 0.034$	$\frac{0.32}{20} = 0.016$	$\frac{0.32}{20} = 0.016$	$mol\,dm^{-3}$

Step 5:

$$K_c = \frac{[PCl_3]_{eq}[Cl_2]_{eq}}{[PCl_5]_{eq}}$$

$$= \frac{0.016\,mol\,dm^{-3} \times 0.016\,mol\,dm^{-3}}{0.034\,mol\,dm^{-3}} = 0.0075\,mol\,dm^{-3}$$

Note that:

- as 32% of the PCl_5 reacted and the initial amount was 1 mol, $0.32 \times 1 = 0.32$ mol reacted. Therefore, the change in moles of PCl_5 was −0.32, so 0.68 mol (1.0 − 0.32) of PCl_5 remained in the equilibrium mixture.
- the molar ratio was 1:1:1. Therefore, if 0.32 mol of PCl_5 reacted, 0.32 mol of PCl_3 and 0.32 mol of Cl_2 were formed.

The calculation is slightly more complicated if the stoichiometric ratio in the equation is not 1:1. Consider the equilibrium:

$$CH_4(g) + 2H_2O(g) \rightleftharpoons CO_2(g) + 4H_2(g)$$

For each mol of methane that reacts, 2 mol of steam are required and 1 mol of carbon dioxide and 4 mol of hydrogen are produced.

Worked example

Chlorine can be produced from hydrogen chloride by the following reaction:

$$4HCl(g) + O_2(g) \rightleftharpoons 2Cl_2(g) + 2H_2O(g)$$

0.40 mol of hydrogen chloride and 0.10 mol of oxygen were placed in a vessel of volume 4.0 dm³ and allowed to reach equilibrium at 400 °C. At equilibrium, only 0.040 mol of hydrogen chloride was present. Calculate the value of K_c.

Answer

$$K_c = \frac{[Cl_2]^2_{eq}[H_2O]^2_{eq}}{[HCl]^4_{eq}[O_2]_{eq}}$$

The moles of hydrogen chloride decreased from 0.40 to 0.040, which is a decrease of 0.36 mol.

	HCl	O₂	Cl₂	H₂O
Initial moles	0.40	0.10	0	0
Change	−0.36	$-\frac{1}{4}(0.36)$ = −0.090	$+\frac{1}{2}(0.36)$ = +0.18	$+\frac{1}{2}(0.36)$ = +0.18
Moles at equilibrium	0.040	0.10 − 0.090 = 0.01	0.18	0.18
Concentration at equilibrium	$\frac{0.040}{4.0}$ = 0.010	$\frac{0.01}{4.0}$ = 0.0025	$\frac{0.18}{4.0}$ = 0.045	$\frac{0.18}{4.0}$ = 0.045

$$K_c = \frac{[Cl_2]^2_{eq}[H_2O]^2_{eq}}{[HCl]^4_{eq}[O_2]_{eq}} = \frac{(0.045\,\text{mol dm}^{-3})^2 \times (0.045\,\text{mol dm}^{-3})^2}{(0.010\,\text{mol dm}^{-3})^4 \times 0.0025\,\text{mol dm}^{-3}}$$

$$= 1.6 \times 10^5\,\text{mol}^{-1}\,\text{dm}^3$$

Note that:

- There were 0.040 moles of HCl at equilibrium and the initial amount was 0.40 mol. Therefore, the amount of HCl that reacted was 0.40 − 0.040 = 0.36 mol. So the change in moles of HCl was −0.36.
- The change in moles of O_2 was one-quarter of the change in moles of HCl, because the ratio of O_2 to HCl in the equation was 1:4.
- The change in moles of Cl_2 (and of H_2O) was half the change in moles of HCl, because the ratio of moles of Cl_2 to HCl in the equation was 2:4.

Expression for K_p

K_p is the equilibrium constant expressed in terms of partial pressures.

For a homogeneous gas phase reaction:

$$xA(g) + yB(g) \rightleftharpoons mC(g) + nD(g)$$

The expression for K_p is:

$$K_p = \frac{p(C)^m p(D)^n}{p(A)^x p(B)^y}$$

where $p(A)$ is the partial pressure of substance A *at equilibrium*.

The units of K_p can be worked out from the expression for K_p by cancelling the units for the individual partial pressure terms.

Remember that the partial pressure of a gas A in a mixture of gases A, B and C is given by:

$$p(A) = \frac{\text{moles of A}}{\text{moles of A + moles of B + moles of C}} \times \text{total pressure}$$

The sum of the partial pressures of all the gases in the system equals the total pressure:

$$p(A) + p(B) + p(C) = \text{total pressure}$$

Worked example

For the equilibrium below, state the expression for K_p and give its units.

$$N_2(g) + 3H_2(g) \rightleftharpoons 2NH_3(g)$$

Answer

$$K_p = \frac{p(NH_3)^2}{p(N_2)p(H_2)^3}$$

The units are:

$$\frac{\text{atm}^2}{\text{atm.atm}^3}$$

$$= \frac{\text{atm}^2}{\text{atm}^4} = \text{atm}^{-2}$$

Calculation of K_p

In K_p calculations, you are always given the chemical equation plus some data, usually the initial amounts and either the amount of one substance at equilibrium or the percentage of a reactant converted. You will also be given the total pressure. You *must* use equilibrium amounts, *not* initial amounts, in your calculation.

The calculation should be carried out in six steps.
- Step 1 — use the chemical equation to write the expression for K_p.
- Step 2 — construct a table and write in the initial number of moles of each substance.
- Step 3 — write in the table the change in moles of each substance and hence work out the number of moles at equilibrium. Add up the moles to find the *total* number of gas moles.
- Step 4 — divide the number of moles of each substance at equilibrium by the total number of moles to obtain the **mole fraction**.
- Step 5 — multiply the mole fraction by the *total* pressure to obtain the partial pressure of each gas.
- Step 6 — substitute the partial pressures into the expression for K_p and work out its value. At the same time, work out the units of K_p and include them in your answer.

Tip For a decomposition equilibrium, such as $PCl_5 \rightleftharpoons PCl_3 + Cl_2$, some questions simply state that a percentage of the reactant has reacted. If so, assume that you started with 1 mol and work from that value.

Worked example

Consider the equilibrium:

$$2SO_2(g) + O_2(g) \rightleftharpoons 2SO_3(g)$$

When 1.6 mol of sulphur dioxide was mixed with 1.2 mol of oxygen and allowed to reach equilibrium at 450 °C, 90% of the sulphur dioxide reacted. The total pressure in the vessel was 7.0 atm. Calculate the value of K_p at this temperature.

Answer

Step 1:

$$K_p = \frac{p(SO_3)^2}{p(SO_2)^2 \times p(O_2)}$$

		SO_2	O_2	SO_3	Total
Step 2	Initial moles	1.6	1.2	0	—
	Change	$-90\% \times 1.6 = -1.44$	$-\frac{1}{2} \times 1.44 = -0.72$	+1.44	—
Step 3	Moles at equilibrium	$1.6 - 1.44 = 0.16$	$1.2 - 0.72 = 0.48$	+1.44	2.08
Step 4	Mole fraction	$\frac{0.16}{2.08} = 0.0769$	$\frac{0.48}{2.08} = 0.231$	$\frac{1.44}{2.08} = 0.692$	—
Step 5	Partial pressure/atm	0.0769×7 $= 0.538$	0.231×7 $= 1.62$	0.692×7 $= 4.84$	—

Step 6:

$$K_p = \frac{p(SO_3)^2}{p(SO_2)^2 p(O_2)} = \frac{(4.84 \text{ atm})^2}{(0.538 \text{ atm})^2 \times 1.62 \text{ atm}} = 50 \text{ atm}^{-1}$$

Note that:
- 90% of the SO_3 reacted, so $0.90 \times 1.6 \text{ mol} = 1.44 \text{ mol reacted}$
- the ratio of O_2 to SO_2 is 1:2, so the moles of O_2 that reacted $= \frac{1}{2} \times 1.44 = 0.72$
- the total number of moles is $0.16 + 0.48 + 1.44 = 2.08$

Calculation of equilibrium partial pressures

For reactions with the same number of gas moles on each side of the equation, the partial pressure of gases at equilibrium can be obtained from K_p and the total pressure.

The method involves:
- letting the partial pressure of one gas be x
- working out the other partial pressures in terms of x and the total pressure, remem- · bering that the sum of all the partial pressures equals the total pressure

Worked example

Equal amounts of hydrogen and iodine are heated in a vessel until equilibrium is reached. Calculate the partial pressures of hydrogen, iodine and hydrogen iodide in an equilibrium mixture produced at a total pressure of 2.0 atm.

$$H_2(g) + I_2(g) \rightleftharpoons 2HI(g) \quad K_p = 49 \text{ (no units)}$$

Answer

Let the partial pressure of hydrogen, $p(H_2)$, at equilibrium $= x$ atm

$p(H_2) = p(I_2)$, so the partial pressure of I_2 is also x atm

$p(HI) + p(H_2) + p(I_2) = $ total pressure $= 2.0$ atm

$p(HI) = 2 - [p(H_2) + p(I_2)] = (2 - 2x)$ atm

$$K_p = \frac{p(HI)^2}{p(H_2)p(I_2)} = \frac{(2-2x)^2}{x^2} = 49$$

Taking square roots of both sides of the equation gives:

$$\frac{(2-2x)}{x} = \sqrt{49} = 7$$

$$7x = 2 - 2x \text{ or } 9x = 2 \text{ or } x = \frac{2}{9} = 0.22$$

Therefore

$p(H_2) = p(I_2) = x = 0.22$ atm

$p(HI) = (2 - 2x) = 2 - 0.44 = 1.56$ atm

Heterogeneous equilibria

In a heterogeneous equilibrium, the reactants and products are in two different phases, for example a gas phase and a solid phase. Solid substances do *not* appear in the expression for the equilibrium constant, because solids do not have a partial pressure.

Consider the reaction:

$$2Fe(s) + 3H_2O(g) \rightleftharpoons Fe_2O_3(s) + 3H_2(g)$$

The expression for K_p is:

$$K_p = \frac{p(H_2)^3}{p(H_2O)^3}$$

Consider the reaction:

$$CaO(s) + CO_2(g) \rightleftharpoons CaCO_3(s)$$

The expression for K_p is:

$$K_p = \frac{1}{p(CO_2)}$$

Factors affecting K and the position of equilibrium

Catalyst

A catalyst:

- has *no* effect on the value of an equilibrium constant
- does not alter the position of equilibrium

- speeds up the forward and reverse reactions equally, so that equilibrium is reached more rapidly

Temperature

- An increase in temperature of an exothermic reaction decreases the value of the equilibrium constant. This results in the position of equilibrium being shifted to the left, lowering the equilibrium yield.
- An increase in temperature causes the position of equilibrium to move in the endothermic direction.
- A decrease in temperature causes the position of equilibrium to move in the exothermic direction.

Consider the reaction:

$$A \rightleftharpoons B \quad \Delta H = -123 \, kJ \, mol^{-1}$$

$$K_c = \frac{[B]_{eq}}{[A]_{eq}}$$

If the temperature is increased, the value of K_c decreases and becomes smaller than the quotient $\frac{[B]}{[A]}$. To restore equilibrium, the quotient must also become smaller. Therefore, some B reacts to form A, until the quotient $\frac{[B]}{[A]}$ once again equals K_c and the system is back in equilibrium.

Consider the reaction:

$$N_2(g) + 3H_2(g) \rightleftharpoons 2NH_3(g) \quad \Delta H = -92.4 \, kJ \, mol^{-1}$$

An increase in temperature causes the equilibrium to shift in the endothermic direction; that is, to the left, lowering the equilibrium yield of ammonia.

In industry, a catalyst is used so that an exothermic reaction can take place quickly at a reduced temperature, thereby increasing the yield.

Pressure

- A change in pressure has *no* effect on the value of the equilibrium constant.
- For reactions with a different number of gas moles on each side of the equation, an increase in pressure will move the position of equilibrium to the side with fewer gas moles.
- A decrease in pressure will move the position of equilibrium to the side with more gas moles.

Consider the reaction:

$$N_2(g) + 3H_2(g) \rightleftharpoons 2NH_3(g)$$

An increase in pressure does *not* alter the value of the equilibrium constant. However, it causes the position of equilibrium to shift to the right (fewer gas moles), thus increasing the equilibrium yield of ammonia.

Acid–base equilibria

Brønsted–Lowry theory of acidity

Acids

An acid is a proton (H^+ ion) donor; it gives an H^+ ion to a base.

Hydrogen chloride is an acid, giving an H^+ ion to a base such as OH^-.

$$HCl + OH^- \longrightarrow H_2O + Cl^-$$

An acid also protonates water, which acts as a base.

$$HCl + H_2O \longrightarrow H_3O^+ + Cl^-$$

Bases

A base accepts H^+ ions. To do this, it must have a lone pair of electrons.

Ammonia is a base, accepting an H^+ ion from an acid such as hydrogen chloride.

$$NH_3 + HCl \longrightarrow NH_4^+ + Cl^-$$

Ammonia is a weak base. It is protonated *reversibly* by water, which acts as an acid.

$$NH_3 + H_2O \rightleftharpoons NH_4^+ + OH^-$$

Conjugate pairs

When an acid loses an H^+ ion, it does so reversibly. The species resulting from the loss of an H^+ is called the **conjugate base** of that acid.

Acid	Conjugate base
HCl	Cl^-
H_2SO_4	HSO_4^-
H_2O	OH^-
CH_3COOH	CH_3COO^-
NH_4^+	NH_3

The species resulting from a base gaining an H^+ ion is called the **conjugate acid** of that base.

Base	Conjugate acid
OH^-	H_2O
H_2O	H_3O^+
NH_3	NH_4^+
$C_2H_5NH_2$	$C_2H_5NH_3^+$
HSO_4^-	H_2SO_4

The equation for an acid–base reaction has an acid on the left with its conjugate base on the right, and a base on the left with its conjugate acid on the right. In this type of reaction there are two acid–base conjugate pairs that you must be able to identify.

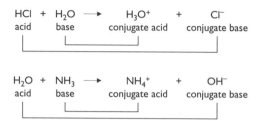

- An acid is linked to its conjugate base by the loss of an H^+ ion.
- A base is linked to its conjugate acid by the gain of an H^+ ion.

Note: water can act either as a base or as an acid.

> **Worked example**
>
> Concentrated nitric acid reacts with concentrated sulphuric acid according to the equation:
>
> $$HNO_3 + H_2SO_4 \longrightarrow H_2NO_3^+ + HSO_4^-$$
>
> Identify the acid–base conjugate pairs in this reaction.
>
> *Answer*
> First pair: acid, H_2SO_4; its conjugate base, HSO_4^-
> Second pair: base, HNO_3; its conjugate acid, $H_2NO_3^+$

pH

Definition of pH

The pH of a solution is defined as the negative logarithm to the base 10 of the hydrogen ion concentration in mol dm^{-3}.

$$pH = -\log[H^+]$$

Thus, if $[H^+] = 1.23 \times 10^{-2}$ mol dm^{-3}, the pH $= -\log[H^+] = -\log(1.23 \times 10^{-2}) = 1.91$

Tip Always give pH values to two decimal places. If you are given the pH, you can calculate $[H^+]$ using the expression

$$[H^+] = 10^{-pH}$$

Thus, if pH = 2.44,

$$[H^+] = 10^{-2.44} = 0.00363 \text{ mol dm}^{-3}$$

You must know how to work this out on your calculator. Remember that $[H^+]$ will normally be less than 1 mol dm^{-3}.

Definition of pOH

The pOH of a solution is defined as the negative logarithm to the base 10 of the hydroxide ion concentration.

$$pOH = -\log[OH^-]$$

K_w and pK_w

Water partially ionises.

$$H_2O \rightleftharpoons H^+ + OH^-$$

$$K_c = \frac{[H^+][OH^-]}{[H_2O]}$$

The concentration of H_2O is so large that it is effectively constant. Therefore, its value can be incorporated into the expression for the equilibrium constant. Thus, the dissociation constant for water, K_w, is defined as:

$K_w = [H^+][OH^-] = 1.0 \times 10^{-14}$ at 25 °C

pK_w = $-\log K_w$ = 14

pK_w = $-\log([H^+][OH^-])$ = pH + pOH

At 25 °C

pH + pOH = 14

The pH of pure water, acidic solutions and alkaline solutions

- Pure water is neutral.
  A *neutral* solution is defined as one in which $[H^+] = [OH^-]$.
  Therefore, $[H^+] = [OH^-] = \sqrt{K_w} = \sqrt{1.0 \times 10^{-14}} = 1.0 \times 10^{-7}$ mol dm^{-3} at 25 °C.
  Therefore, the pH of a neutral solution at 25 °C = $-\log(1.0 \times 10^{-7})$ = 7.00.
- An *acidic* solution is defined as one in which $[H^+] > [OH^-]$.
  Therefore, $[H^+] > 1.0 \times 10^{-7}$, which means that pH < 7.
- An *alkaline* solution is defined as one where $[H^+] < [OH^-]$.
  Therefore, $[H^+] < 1.0 \times 10^{-7}$, resulting in a pH > 7.
  If a solution has $[H^+] = 3.0 \times 10^{-9}$ mol dm^{-3}, the pH = $-\log(3.0 \times 10^{-9})$ = 8.52 and it is alkaline.

Calculation of pH of an alkaline solution

The pH of an alkaline solution can be calculated from $[OH^-]$. For example:

$[OH^-] = 2.2 \times 10^{-2}$ mol dm^{-3}

pOH = $-\log[OH^-]$ = $-\log(2.2 \times 10^{-2})$ = 1.66

pH + pOH = 14

pH = 14 $-$ pOH = 14 $-$ 1.66 = 12.34

An alternative method is:

$[OH^-] = 2.2 \times 10^{-2}$ mol dm^{-3}

$[H^+][OH^-] = 1.0 \times 10^{-14}$

$$[H^+] = \frac{1.0 \times 10^{-14}}{[OH^-]} = \frac{1.0 \times 10^{-14}}{2.2 \times 10^{-2}} = 4.55 \times 10^{-13}$$

pH = $-\log [H^+]$ = $-\log(4.55 \times 10^{-13})$ = 12.34

pH scale

- Neutral solutions: $[H^+] = [OH^-]$; pH = 7.00 (at 25 °C)
- Acidic solutions: $[H^+] > [OH^-]$; pH < 7
- Alkaline solutions: $[H^+] < [OH^-]$; pH > 7

The pH scale runs from negative numbers to above 14. A small change in hydrogen ion or hydroxide ion concentration causes a large pH change in a solution with an initial pH close to 7. A pH change from 1 to 0 is the result of a change in hydrogen ion concentration from 0.1 to 1 mol dm^{-3} (a change of 0.9 mol dm^{-3}). A pH change from 6 to 5 is the result of a change in hydrogen ion concentration from 0.000001 to 0.00001 mol dm^{-3}, an increase of only 0.000009 mol dm^{-3}.

pH at 25 °C	[H$^+$]/mol dm^{-3}	Acidity
Negative	> 1	Very strongly acidic
0 to 2	1 to 10^{-2}	Strongly acidic
2 to 5	10^{-2} to 10^{-5}	Weakly acidic
6	10^{-6}	Very weakly acidic
7	10^{-7}	Neutral

pH at 25 °C	[OH$^-$]/mol dm^{-3}	Alkalinity
7	10^{-7}	Neutral
8	10^{-6}	Very weakly alkaline
9 to 12	10^{-5} to 10^{-2}	Weakly alkaline
12 to 14	10^{-2} to 1	Strongly alkaline
Above 14	> 1	Very strongly alkaline

Strong acids and bases

Strong acids

A strong acid, such as hydrochloric acid, is totally ionised in aqueous solution.

$$HCl + aq \longrightarrow H^+(aq) + Cl^-(aq)$$

Thus, [H$^+$] = the initial concentration of the acid.
- Hydrochloric acid, hydrobromic acid, HBr, and hydroiodic acid, HI, are all strong acids.
- Nitric acid, HNO$_3$, is also a strong acid.
- Sulphuric acid, H$_2$SO$_4$, is strong from its *first* ionisation only.

$$H_2SO_4 + aq \longrightarrow H^+(aq) + HSO_4^-(aq)$$

- The pH of an acid can be negative if its concentration is more than 1 mol dm^{-3}. For instance, the pH of a 2.00 mol dm^{-3} solution of HCl = $-\log(2.00)$ = -0.30.

Worked example

Calculate the pH of the strong monobasic acid HCl of concentration 0.123 mol dm^{-3}.

Answer

pH = $-\log$[H$^+$] = $-\log(0.123)$ = 0.91

---

content guidance

Strong bases

Strong bases are totally ionised in solution. For example:

$NaOH + aq \longrightarrow Na^+(aq) + OH^-(aq)$

$Ba(OH)_2 + aq \longrightarrow Ba^{2+}(aq) + 2OH^-(aq)$

For strong bases with one OH^- ion per formula, the OH^- ion concentration is equal to the initial concentration of the base. For bases with two OH^- ions per formula, the OH^- ion concentration is twice the initial concentration of the base.

There are two ways of calculating the pH.

Worked example 1

Calculate the pH of a $2.00\,mol\,dm^{-3}$ solution of sodium hydroxide.

Answer using method 1

$[OH^-] = 2.00\,mol\,dm^{-3}$

$pOH = -log[OH^-] = -log(2.00) = -0.30$

$pH = 14 - pOH = 14 - (-0.30) = 14.30$

Answer using method 2

$[OH^-] = 2.00\,mol\,dm^{-3}$

$[H^+] = \dfrac{1.0 \times 10^{-14}}{[OH^-]} = \dfrac{1.0 \times 10^{-14}}{2.00} = 5.00 \times 10^{-15}$

$pH = -log[H^+] = -log(5.00 \times 10^{-15}) = 14.30$

Worked example 2

Calculate the pH of a $0.222\,mol\,dm^{-3}$ solution of $Ba(OH)_2$.

Answer using method 1

$[OH^-] = 2 \times 0.222 = 0.444\,mol\,dm^{-3}$

$pOH = -log[OH^-] = -log(0.444) = 0.35$

$pH = 14 - pOH = 14 - 0.35 = 13.65$

Answer using method 2

$[OH^-] = 2 \times 0.222 = 0.444\,mol\,dm^{-3}$

$[H^+] = \dfrac{1.0 \times 10^{-14}}{0.444} = 2.25 \times 10^{-14}\,mol\,dm^{-3}$

$pH = -log[H^+] = -log(2.25 \times 10^{-14}) = 13.65$

Weak acids

A weak acid is only *slightly* ionised. For dilute solutions of most weak acids, the extent of ionisation is less than 10%, so most of the acid is present as un-ionised molecules.

$CH_3COOH + aq \rightleftharpoons H_3O^+(aq) + CH_3COO^-(aq)$

Enthalpy of neutralisation of weak acids

The enthalpy of neutralisation of a weak acid, HA, is *less* exothermic than that for a strong acid. You can regard the process of neutralisation of a weak acid as taking place in two steps:

$$HA \rightleftharpoons H^+ + A^- \qquad \Delta H = +x \, kJ \, mol^{-1}$$
$$H^+ + OH^- \longrightarrow H_2O \qquad \Delta H = \Delta H_{neutralisation} \text{ of a strong acid} = -57 \, kJ \, mol^{-1}$$
$$HA + OH^- \longrightarrow A^- + H_2O \qquad \Delta H = \Delta H_{neutralisation} \text{ of the weak acid HA}$$
$$= x + (-57) \, kJ \, mol^{-1}, \text{ which is less exothermic}$$
$$\text{than } -57 \, kJ \, mol^{-1}, \text{ the } \Delta H_{neutralisation} \text{ of a strong}$$
$$\text{acid}$$

pH of weak acids

This concept is easier to follow if the formula of a weak acid is represented by HA. HA ionises reversibly according to:

$$HA \rightleftharpoons H^+ + A^- \text{ or } HA + H_2O \rightleftharpoons H_3O^+ + A^-$$

The acid dissociation constant, K_a, is given by:

$$K_a = \frac{[H^+][A^-]}{[HA]} \text{ or } \frac{[H_3O^+][A^-]}{[HA]} \, mol \, dm^{-3}$$

The pK_a of a weak acid is defined as $-\log K_a$, so $K_a = 10^{-pK}$.

Tip You may use H^+, $H^+(aq)$ or H_3O^+ in the chemical equation and in the expression for K_a.

As the acid is only slightly ionised, you can make the approximation:
    [HA] = the initial concentration of the weak acid

The ionisation of 1 molecule of HA produces one H^+ ion and one A^- ion.
    $[H^+] = [A^-]$

The expression for K_a becomes:

$$K_a = \frac{[H^+]^2}{[HA]}$$

$$[H^+] = \sqrt{K_a[HA]} = \sqrt{K_a \times \text{initial concentration of weak acid}}$$

Therefore, the pH of a weak acid can be calculated from its concentration and its acid dissociation constant.

Worked example

Calculate the pH of a 0.123 mol dm^{-3} solution of ethanoic acid.
$K_a = 1.74 \times 10^{-5}$ mol dm^{-3}.

Answer

$$CH_3COOH \rightleftharpoons H^+ + CH_3COO^-$$

$$K_a = \frac{[H^+][CH_3COO^-]}{[CH_3COOH]} = \frac{[H^+]^2}{[CH_3COOH]} = 1.74 \times 10^{-5} \, mol \, dm^{-3}$$

$$[H^+] = \sqrt{(K_a[CH_3COOH])} = \sqrt{(1.74 \times 10^{-5} \times 0.123)} = 0.00146 \, mol \, dm^{-3}$$

$$pH = -\log[H^+] = -\log(0.00146) = 2.83$$

Tip The pK_a of the acid may be given instead of its K_a value. In this case, use $K_a = 10^{-pK}$ — for example:

- pK_a for methanoic acid (HCOOH) = 3.75
- K_a for methanoic acid = $10^{-3.75} = 1.78 \times 10^{-4} \, \text{mol dm}^{-3}$

Calculation of K_a from pH

This is a similar calculation to the previous one. If you are given the pH and the concentration of a solution, K_a can be calculated.

> **Worked example**
>
> Calculate the acid dissociation constant for a weak acid, HA, given that a $0.106 \, \text{mol dm}^{-3}$ solution has a pH of 3.21.
>
> *Answer*
>
> $$K_a = \frac{[H^+][A^-]}{[HA]}$$
>
> $[H^+] = 10^{-pH} = 10^{-3.21} = 6.166 \times 10^{-4} \, \text{mol dm}^{-3} = [A^-]$
>
> $[HA] = 0.106 - 0.0006166 = 0.1054 \, \text{mol dm}^{-3}$
>
> $$K_a = \frac{(6.166 \times 10^{-4})^2}{0.1054} = 3.61 \times 10^{-6} \, \text{mol dm}^{-3}$$
>
> *Note*: as 6.166×10^{-4} moles of H^+ ions are produced from 0.106 mol of HA, the amount of HA at equilibrium equals $(0.106 - 6.166 \times 10^{-4}) = 0.1054 \, \text{mol}$. A less accurate value of K_a can be calculated using $[HA] = 0.106 \, \text{mol dm}^{-3}$.

pH of sulphuric acid

Sulphuric acid is a strong acid from its first ionisation, but a weak acid from its second.

$$H_2SO_4 \longrightarrow H^+ + HSO_4^-$$
$$HSO_4^- \rightleftharpoons H^+ + SO_4^{2-}$$

The second ionisation is driven to the left (suppressed) by the high concentration of H^+ from the first ionisation. Hence, the pH of a $0.1 \, \text{mol dm}^{-3}$ solution of sulphuric acid is only just below 1, as $0.1 \, \text{mol dm}^{-3}$ of H^+ ions is produced from the first ionisation and hardly any from the second ionisation.

Acid–base titrations

There are several factors to consider.

- The usual method is to add a standard solution of base from a burette to a known volume of acid, in the presence of a suitable indicator. The addition of base is normally stopped when the 'end point' has been reached.
- The end point is reached when enough base has been added to react totally with the acid. The pH at the end point is 7, only when a strong base is titrated with a strong acid.
- The word 'neutralise' is often used. However, the end point is on the acidic side of neutral if a weak base, such as ammonia solution, is titrated with a strong acid and above 7 if a strong base is titrated with a weak acid.

Titration	pH at end point	Common indicators
Strong acid–strong base	7	Methyl orange, methyl red or phenolphthalein
Strong acid–weak base	5–6	Methyl orange or methyl red
Weak acid–strong base	8–9	Phenolphthalein

- Acid–base titrations can also be carried out by adding a standard solution of acid from a burette to a known volume of base.

Titration curves

These need to be drawn carefully. Follow these steps:
- Decide whether the acid and base are strong or weak.
- Draw the axes. The y-axis (vertical) should be labelled 'pH', with a linear scale, and the x-axis labelled 'volume of solution being added' (normally the base). Some questions ask for the titration curve when acid is added to a base, in which case the x-axis represents the volume of acid.
- Calculate the volume that has to be added to reach the end point. In most questions, the concentrations of acid and base are the same; therefore, the volume of base at the end point will be the same as the initial volume of acid.
- Estimate the pH:
  - at the start
  - at the end point
  - of the vertical range of the curve
  - after excess base has been added (final pH)
- Draw a smooth curve with the vertical section at the end point volume.

The table below shows pH values duing typical titrations.

Type of titration	Starting pH	End point pH	Vertical range pH	Final pH
Strong acid added to strong base	1	7	3–11	13
Strong base added to strong acid	13	7	3–11	1
Strong acid added to weak base	1	5	3–7	11
Weak base added to strong acid	11	5	3–7	1
Weak acid added to strong base	3	9	7–11	13
Strong base added to weak acid	13	9	7–11	3

The six graphs below are examples of titration curves. In each case, the left-hand graph shows the change in pH when $40 \, cm^3$ of base is added to $20 \, cm^3$ of acid, both having the same concentration. The right-hand graph is for the addition of acid to $20 \, cm^3$ of base. The end point is $20 \, cm^3$ in each case.

Strong acid–strong base

For example, hydrochloric acid and sodium hydroxide:

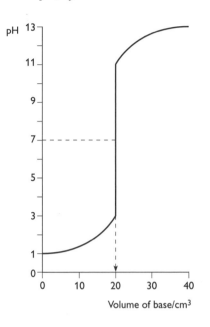

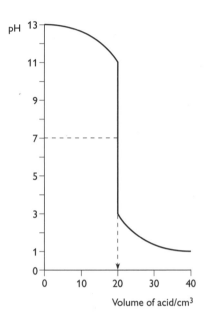

Strong acid–weak base

For example, hydrochloric acid and ammonia solution:

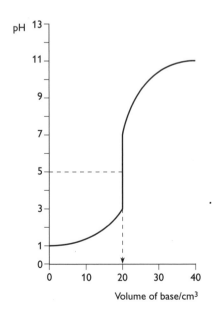

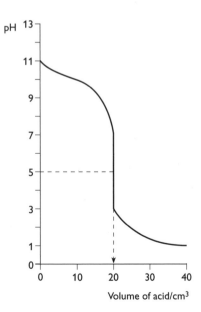

Weak acid–strong base

For example, ethanoic acid and sodium hydroxide:

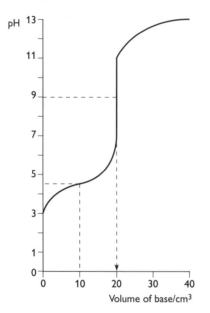

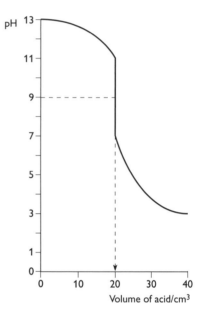

Calculation of pKₐ from titration curves

When a strong base is added to a solution of a weak acid, the value of pK_a can be found by reading off the pH at the point when *half* the acid has been neutralised by the alkali (halfway to the end-point volume).

At this point:

$$[HA]_{halfway} = [A^-]_{halfway}$$

$$K_a = \frac{[H^+][A^-]}{[HA]}$$

At the halfway point:

$$K_a = [H^+]_{halfway}$$
$$pK_a = (pH)_{halfway}$$

In the titration curve for a strong base being added to a weak acid, $pK_a = 4.5$.

Indicators

Indicators are weak acids in which the acid molecule, represented by the formula HInd, is a different colour from its conjugate base, Ind⁻.

$$HInd \rightleftharpoons H^+ + Ind^-$$

An example is methyl orange. The acid, HInd, is red and its conjugate base, Ind⁻, is yellow.

$$K_{ind} = \frac{[H^+][Ind^-]}{[HInd]}$$

At the end-point colour, the acid and its conjugate base are in equal proportions. Therefore:

$[HInd] = [Ind^-]$

$K_{ind} = [H^+]_{end\ point}$

$pK_{ind} = (pH)_{end\ point}$

Most indicators noticeably change colour over a range of ± 1 pH unit. Methyl orange, $pK_{ind} = 3.7$, is red below a pH of 2.7, gradually changes to orange at pH 3.7 and then to yellow at pH 4.7.

Choice of indicator

The pH range over which an indicator changes colour must lie *completely within* the vertical part of the titration curve.

- For a strong acid–strong base titration, any indicator with pK_{ind} value from 3.5 to 10.5 has its range completely within the vertical part and is therefore suitable. Thus, methyl red ($pK_{ind} = 5.1$), methyl orange ($pK_{ind} = 3.7$) and phenolphthalein ($pK_{ind} = 9.3$) are all suitable.
- For a strong acid–weak base titration, the indicator must have a pK_{ind} value from 3.5 to 6.5 to be suitable. Thus, methyl red ($pK_{ind} = 5.1$) and methyl orange ($pK_{ind} = 3.7$) are both suitable.
- For a weak acid–strong base titration, the indicator must have a pK_{ind} value between pH 6.5 and 10.5. Phenolphthalein ($pK_{ind} = 9.3$) is suitable.

Buffer solutions

A buffer solution *resists* a change in pH when *small* amounts of acid or base are added. It is made up of a weak acid and its conjugate base, or a weak base and its conjugate acid. Examples are:

- ethanoic acid (CH_3COOH) plus sodium ethanoate ($CH_3COO^-Na^+$), which is an acid buffer with a pH less than 7
- ammonia solution (NH_3) plus ammonium chloride ($NH_4^+Cl^-$), which is an alkaline buffer with a pH greater than 7

A buffer solution is at its most efficient when:

- for an acidic buffer, the concentration of the weak acid equals the concentration of its conjugate base
- for an alkaline buffer, the concentration of the weak base equals the concentration of its conjugate acid

Tip Do not say that a buffer has constant pH, because the pH *does* alter slightly when small amounts of acid or base are added.

Mode of action of a buffer solution

Acid buffer

The ethanoic acid–sodium ethanoate buffer system is used as an example. The weak acid is *partially* ionised.

$$CH_3COOH \rightleftharpoons H^+ + CH_3COO^-$$

Its salt, which contains the conjugate base, is *totally* ionised.

$$CH_3COONa \longrightarrow CH_3COO^- + Na^+$$

The CH_3COO^- ions produced suppress the ionisation of the weak acid. Therefore, if the weak acid and its salt are present in similar molar amounts:

$[CH_3COOH]$ = [weak acid]

$[CH_3COO^-]$ = [salt of weak acid]

If a *small* quantity of H^+ ions is added, almost all react with the large reservoir of CH_3COO^- ions from the salt, and so $[H^+]$ and the pH hardly change.

$$H^+ + CH_3COO^- \longrightarrow CH_3COOH$$

If a *small* amount of OH^- ions is added to the buffer solution, almost all of them react with the large reservoir of CH_3COOH molecules from the acid and so $[OH]^-$ and hence the pH hardly change.

$$OH^- + CH_3COOH \longrightarrow H_2O + CH_3COO^-$$

The crucial points that must be made when explaining the mode of action of a buffer are that:

- the weak acid ionises *reversibly* (equation needed)
- the salt ionises *totally* (equation needed) and suppresses the ionisation of the acid, which results in relatively large reservoirs of both the weak acid and its conjugate base
- almost all the added H^+ ions are removed by reaction with the conjugate base (equation needed)
- almost all the added OH^- ions are removed by reaction with the weak acid (equation needed)

Alkaline buffer

An alkaline buffer works in a similar way. The weak base (ammonia) mops up most of the added H^+ ions and its conjugate acid (ammonium ion, NH_4^+) mops up most of the added OH^- ions. The equations are:

$$H^+ + NH_3 \rightleftharpoons NH_4^+$$

$$OH^- + NH_4^+ \longrightarrow H_2O + NH_3$$

Calculation of pH of a buffer solution

Calculation of the pH of a buffer solution relies on the relationship between K_a and the concentrations of the weak acid and its salt.

$$K_a = \frac{[H^+][\text{salt of weak acid}]}{[\text{weak acid}]}$$

$$[H^+] = \frac{K_a[\text{weak acid}]}{[\text{salt of weak acid}]}$$

The pH is then calculated as $-\log[H^+]$.

The standard calculation is to work out the pH, given the volume of a weak acid solution of known concentration and the mass of its salt.

Worked example 1

Calculate the pH of a buffer solution made by adding 6.15 g of sodium ethanoate, CH_3COONa (molar mass $82\,g\,mol^{-1}$), to $50.0\,cm^3$ of a $1.00\,mol\,dm^{-3}$ solution of ethanoic acid ($K_a = 1.75 \times 10^{-5}\,mol\,dm^{-3}$).

Answer

$$K_a = \frac{[H^+][CH_3COO^-]}{[CH_3COOH]} = \frac{[H^+][\text{salt of weak acid}]}{[\text{weak acid}]}$$

or

$$[H^+] = \frac{K_a[\text{weak acid}]}{[\text{salt of weak acid}]} = \frac{K_a[CH_3COOH]}{[CH_3COONa]}$$

$[CH_3COOH] = 1.00\,mol\,dm^{-3}$

$$\text{amount of sodium ethanoate} = \frac{6.15\,g}{82\,g\,mol^{-1}} = 0.075\,mol$$

$$[CH_3COONa] = \frac{0.075\,mol}{0.050\,dm^3} = 1.50\,mol\,dm^{-3}$$

$$[H^+] = \frac{1.75 \times 10^{-5}\,mol\,dm^{-3} \times 1.00\,mol\,dm^{-3}}{1.50\,mol\,dm^{-3}} = 1.17 \times 10^{-5}\,mol\,dm^{-3}$$

$pH = -\log(1.17 \times 10^{-5}) = 4.93$

A more difficult calculation is when a known volume of strong base solution is added to an excess of weak acid solution. This forms a mixture of excess weak acid and its salt.

Worked example 2

Calculate the pH of a buffer solution made by adding $50\,cm^3$ of $1.00\,mol\,dm^{-3}$ solution of sodium hydroxide to $80\,cm^3$ of $1.00\,mol\,dm^{-3}$ solution of propanoic acid, CH_3CH_2COOH, $K_a = 1.35 \times 10^{-5}\,mol\,dm^{-3}$.

Answer

amount of sodium hydroxide added $= 1.00\,mol\,dm^{-3} \times 0.050\,dm^3$
$= 0.050\,mol$
$= $ amount of sodium propanoate produced

amount of propanoic acid initially $= 1.00\,mol\,dm^{-3} \times 0.080\,dm^3$
$= 0.080\,mol$

amount of propanoic acid *left* after reaction with sodium hydroxide $= 0.080 - 0.050$
$= 0.030\,mol$

$$[CH_3CH_2COOH] = \frac{0.030\,mol}{0.130\,dm^3} = 0.231\,mol\,dm^{-3}$$

$$[CH_3CH_2COONa] = \frac{0.050\,mol}{0.130\,dm^3} = 0.385\,mol\,dm^{-3}$$

$$K_a = \frac{[H^+][CH_3CH_2COO^-]}{[CH_3CH_2COOH]} = \frac{[H^+][\text{salt of weak acid}]}{[\text{weak acid}]}$$

$$[H^+] = \frac{K_a [\text{weak acid}]}{[\text{salt of weak acid}]}$$

$$[H^+] = \frac{1.35 \times 10^{-5} \text{ mol dm}^{-3} \times 0.231 \text{ mol dm}^{-3}}{0.385 \text{ mol dm}^{-3}} = 8.10 \times 10^{-6} \text{ mol dm}^{-3}$$

$$pH = -\log(8.10 \times 10^{-6}) = 5.09$$

Note that:
- propanoic acid and sodium hydroxide react in a 1:1 ratio to produce sodium propanoate and water
- the total volume of the solution is $50 + 80 = 130 \text{ cm}^3 = 0.130 \text{ dm}^3$

Organic chemistry

Required AS chemistry

Nomenclature

You should refresh your knowledge of how organic compounds are named.

Carbon chain length	Stem name
One atom	Meth-
Two atoms	Eth-
Three atoms	Prop-
Four atoms	But-
Five atoms	Pent-

If the chain contains three or more carbon atoms, the position of a functional group is indicated by a number — for example: $CH_3CH_2CH=CH_2$ is but-1-ene; $CH_3CH(OH)CH_3$ is propan-2-ol.

If the carbon chain is *branched,* the position of the alkyl branch is indicated by a number. For example, $CH_3CH_2CH(CH_3)CH_2CH_2OH$ is 3-methylpentan-1-ol.

Bond enthalpy and polarity

The smaller the value of the bond enthalpy, the weaker is the bond. This means that the activation enthalpy of a reaction involving the breaking of that bond will be lower and the rate of reaction faster. For example, the C–I bond is weaker than the C–Cl bond, so iodoalkanes react faster than chloroalkanes.

The π-bond in alkenes is weaker than the σ-bond in alkanes, so alkenes are more reactive than alkanes.

The bond polarity determines the type of reaction. The carbon atom in halogenoalkanes is δ+, so it is attacked by nucleophiles.

Reaction types

Type of reaction	Examples
Free radical substitution	Alkanes with halogens
Free radical addition	Polymerisation of alkenes
Electrophilic addition	Alkenes with halogens or hydrogen halides
Nucleophilic substitution	Halogenoalkanes with aqueous OH⁻, CN⁻ or ammonia
Elimination	Water from alcohols
	Hydrogen halide from halogenoalkanes
Hydrolysis	Halogenoalkanes with aqueous sodium hydroxide
Reduction	Alkenes with hydrogen
Oxidation	Alcohols with acidified potassium dichromate(VI)
	Alkenes with potassium manganate(VII)
Polymerisation	Alkenes to give poly(alkenes)

Reactions, reagents and conditions

Alkanes

In the presence of light, alkanes react with chlorine — for example:

$$CH_4 + Cl_2 \longrightarrow CH_3Cl + HCl$$

The organic product is chloromethane.

Alkenes

In the table below, propene is used as the example.

Reagent	Equation	Conditions	Organic product
Hydrogen	$CH_3CH=CH_2 + H_2 \longrightarrow$ $CH_3CH_2CH_3$	Heated nickel catalyst	Propane
Bromine	$CH3CH=CH2 + Br2 \longrightarrow$ $CH_3CHBrCH_2Br$	Bubble propene into bromine dissolved in hexane	1,2-dibromopropane
Hydrogen chloride	$CH_3CH=CH_2 + HCl \longrightarrow$ $CH_3CHClCH_3$	Mix gases at room temperature	2-chloropropane
Potassium manganate(VII) (oxidation)	$CH_3CH=CH_2 + [O]$ $+ H_2O \longrightarrow$ $CH_3CH(OH)CH_2OH$	Neutral aqueous solution	Propane-1,2-diol

Halogenoalkanes

In the table below, 1-bromopropane is used as the example.

Reagent	Equation	Conditions	Organic product
Aqueous sodium (or potassium) hydroxide	$CH_3CH_2CH_2Br$ + NaOH ⟶ $CH_3CH_2CH_2OH$ + NaBr	Heat under reflux in *aqueous* solution	Propan-1-ol
Ethanolic potassium hydroxide	$CH_3CH_2CH_2Br$ + KOH ⟶ $CH_3CH=CH_2$ + KBr + H_2O	Heat under reflux in *ethanolic* solution	Propene
Potassium cyanide	$CH_3CH_2CH_2Br$ + KCN ⟶ $CH_3CH_2CH_2CN$ + KBr	Heat under reflux in a solution of water and ethanol	Butanenitrile
Ammonia	$CH_3CH_2CH_2Br$ + $2NH_3$ ⟶ $CH_3CH_2CH_2NH_2$+ NH_4Br	Heat in a sealed tube with a concentrated solution of ammonia	1-propylamine

Alcohols

In the table below, ethanol is used as the example.

Reagent	Equation	Conditions	Organic product
Potassium dichromate(VI) (oxidation)	CH_3CH_2OH + 2[O] ⟶ CH_3COOH + H_2O	Heat under reflux with sulphuric acid	Ethanoic acid
	CH_3CH_2OH + [O] ⟶ CH_3CHO + H_2O	Add hot sulphuric acid and distil off product as it forms	Ethanal
Concentrated sulphuric acid (dehydration)	CH_3CH_2OH – H_2O ⟶ $CH_2=CH_2$	Heat to 170 °C	Ethene
Phosphorus(V) chloride	CH_3CH_2OH + PCl_5 ⟶ CH_3CH_2Cl + HCl + $POCl_3$	Dry reagents at room temperature	Chloroethane
Hydrogen bromide	CH_3CH_2OH + HBr ⟶ CH_3CH_2Br + H_2O	HBr is made by adding 50% sulphuric acid to solid potassium bromide	Bromoethane

Note: secondary alcohols are oxidised to ketones by potassium dichromate(VI); tertiary alcohols do not react.

Isomerism

Isomers have the same molecular formula, but the atoms are arranged differently within the molecule.

Structural isomerism

- **Carbon chain** — the isomers have different carbon chain lengths. For instance, butane ($CH_3CH_2CH_2CH_3$) and methylpropane ($CH_3CH(CH_3)CH_3$) have the same molecular formula, C_4H_{10}.

- **Positional** — the same functional group is in a different position in the isomers, for example propan-1-ol ($CH_3CH_2CH_2OH$) and propan-2-ol ($CH_3CH(OH)CH_3$).
- **Functional group** — the isomers are members of different homologous series. Examples are:
  - propanoic acid (CH_3CH_2COOH) and methylethanoate (CH_3COOCH_3)
  - ethanol (C_2H_5OH) and methoxymethane (CH_3OCH_3)

Tip If you are asked to draw a *full* structural formula, you must draw each individual atom and bond.

Geometric isomerism

Geometric (*cis–trans*) isomerism is a form of **stereoisomerism**. In an alkene, geometric isomerism is the result of restricted rotation about a carbon–carbon double bond, provided that the two groups on each atom of the C=C group are different from each other.

The π-overlap in a double bond is above and below the plane of the molecule. Therefore, it is not possible to rotate about the double bond without breaking the π-bond, which only happens at high temperatures. Hence, the *cis* and *trans* isomers are different.

A2 chemistry

Optical isomerism

Optical isomerism is another form of stereoisomerism. It is the result of four different groups being attached to a carbon atom. This carbon atom is called the **chiral centre** and results in **chirality**. A chiral molecule is defined as a molecule that is non-superimposable on its mirror image.

Mirror

Tip You must draw the two isomers as mirror images of each other, with wedges and with dots or dashes to give a three-dimensional appearance to your drawing. Make sure that you do not draw a bond to the wrong atom, for instance to the H of a $-CH_3$, $-OH$ or $-COOH$ group.

Optical isomers can be distinguished from each other because they rotate the plane of plane-polarised light in opposite directions.

Most chemical reactions result in a **racemic** (50:50) mixture of the two optical isomers. Such a mixture does not have any effect on polarised light.

Reactions of organic compounds

Grignard reagents

Grignard reagents are organometallic compounds in which a magnesium atom is bound to both an alkyl group and a halogen — for example, ethylmagnesium bromide, CH_3CH_2MgBr.

Preparation

A halogenoalkane is mixed with dry ether (ethoxyethane) and placed in a round-bottomed flask fitted with a reflux condenser. Some magnesium is then added. If the reaction does not start, a single crystal of iodine is added as a catalyst. The reaction is exothermic and fairly rapid.

$$C_2H_5Br + Mg \longrightarrow C_2H_5MgBr$$

The Grignard reagent is never isolated — it is used immediately.

Water must be excluded as the Grignard reagent is rapidly hydrolysed by even a trace of water, forming an alkane.

$$C_2H_5MgBr + H_2O \longrightarrow C_2H_6 + Mg(OH)Br$$

Reactions

In all reactions, the Grignard reagent adds on to a C=O group. This adduct then has to be hydrolysed by adding dilute acid to give the required organic product. The δ– carbon atom in the Grignard reagent attacks the δ+ carbon atom in the C=O group, forming a new carbon–carbon σ-bond, thereby increasing the carbon chain length.

The reactions are examples of **nucleophilic addition** by the Grignard reagent to carbon dioxide, aldehydes or ketones. The C=O group becomes a C–OH group and the alkyl part of the Grignard reagent (for example, the C_2H_5 group) attaches to the same carbon atom.

Reaction with cold, solid carbon dioxide

When a solution of a Grignard reagent is added, followed by the addition of dilute hydrochloric acid, a carboxylic acid is produced. The overall equation is:

$$CO_2 + C_2H_5MgBr + HCl \longrightarrow C_2H_5COOH + MgBrCl$$

The organic product is propanoic acid.

Reaction with methanal, HCHO

The dry reagents are mixed, followed by dilute hydrochloric acid. A primary alcohol is produced. The overall equation is:

$$HCHO + C_2H_5MgBr + HCl \longrightarrow C_2H_5CH_2OH + MgBrCl$$

The organic product is propan-1-ol.

Reaction with aldehydes, such as ethanal, CH_3CHO

The dry reagents are mixed, followed by the addition of dilute hydrochloric acid. A secondary alcohol is produced. For example:

$$CH_3CH_2 - \overset{\overset{\displaystyle H}{|}}{\underset{\underset{\displaystyle OH}{|}}{C}} - CH_3$$

Reaction with ketones, such as propanone, CH_3COCH_3

The dry reagents are mixed, followed by the addition of dilute hydrochloric acid. A tertiary alcohol is produced — for example:

$$CH_3 - CH_2 - \overset{\overset{\displaystyle CH_3}{|}}{\underset{\underset{\displaystyle OH}{|}}{C}} - CH_3$$

Carboxylic acids

Carboxylic acids contain the –COOH group.

$$-\overset{\overset{\displaystyle O}{\parallel}}{C}\diagdown_{\displaystyle O - H}$$

Their general formula is $C_nH_{2n+1}COOH$, or RCOOH, where R is an alkyl group.

They are all weak acids, and so they are only slightly ionised in water.

$$RCOOH + H_2O \rightleftharpoons H_3O^+ + RCOO^-$$

Preparation
Oxidation of primary alcohols

When a primary alcohol is heated under reflux with a solution of potassium dichromate(VI) in sulphuric acid, it is oxidised to a carboxylic acid.

$$CH_3CH_2CH_2OH + 2[O] \longrightarrow CH_3CH_2COOH + H_2O$$

Hydrolysis of nitriles

When a nitrile is heated under reflux with a dilute acid such as hydrochloric acid, it is hydrolysed to a carboxylic acid.

$$CH_3CH_2CN + 2H_2O + HCl \longrightarrow CH_3CH_2COOH + NH_4Cl$$

Reactions of ethanoic acid, CH_3COOH
Reaction with bases

- Ethanoic acid reacts with aqueous sodium hydroxide to give a salt, sodium ethanoate.

$$CH_3COOH + NaOH \longrightarrow CH_3COO^-Na^+ + H_2O$$

- It reacts with sodium carbonate (solid or in solution), giving off carbon dioxide.

$$2CH_3COOH + Na_2CO_3 \longrightarrow 2CH_3COO^-Na^+ + H_2O + CO_2$$

- It reacts with aqueous sodium hydrogen carbonate, giving off bubbles of carbon dioxide.

$$CH_3COOH + NaHCO_3 \longrightarrow CH_3COO^-Na^+ + H_2O + CO_2$$

This reaction is a test for an acid.

Reaction with alcohols

When ethanoic acid is warmed under reflux with an alcohol in the presence of a few drops of concentrated sulphuric acid catalyst, an ester is formed. With methanol, methyl ethanoate is produced.

$$CH_3COOH + CH_3OH \rightleftharpoons CH_3COOCH_3 + H_2O$$

If the products of this reaction are poured into cold water, the characteristic sweet smell of an ester can be detected.

Reaction with phosphorus(V) chloride

If phosphorus(V) chloride is added to a dry sample of ethanoic acid, steamy fumes of hydrogen chloride are given off and an acid chloride is produced. The organic product is ethanoyl chloride.

$$CH_3COOH + PCl_5 \longrightarrow CH_3COCl + HCl + POCl_3$$

Reaction with lithium aluminium hydride

Carboxylic acids are reduced to primary alcohols by lithium aluminium hydride. This is a two-stage process. The first stage is to add lithium aluminium hydride to a solution of the organic acid in dry ether. The second is to hydrolyse the adduct formed with dilute hydrochloric acid. The reducing agent is represented by [H] in the overall equation:

$$CH_3COOH + 4[H] \longrightarrow CH_3CH_2OH + H_2O$$

Acid chlorides

Acid chlorides contain the group:

The carbon atom of the C=O group is $\delta+$. Therefore, acid chlorides react with nucleophiles.

Reactions

Reaction with water

Acid chlorides are hydrolysed by water. The carboxylic acid is produced — for example:

$$CH_3COCl + H_2O \longrightarrow CH_3COOH + HCl$$

Reaction with alcohols

On mixing, a rapid reaction takes place at room temperature and an ester is formed. For example, ethanoyl chloride reacts with propan-1-ol to form 1-propylethanoate.

$$CH_3COCl + CH_3CH_2CH_2OH \longrightarrow CH_3COOCH_2CH_2CH_3 + HCl$$

This is a rapid and complete reaction, unlike the slow, reversible esterification of a carboxylic acid with an alcohol.

A **polyester** is made by reacting molecules containing two acid chloride groups with molecules containing two alcoholic groups.

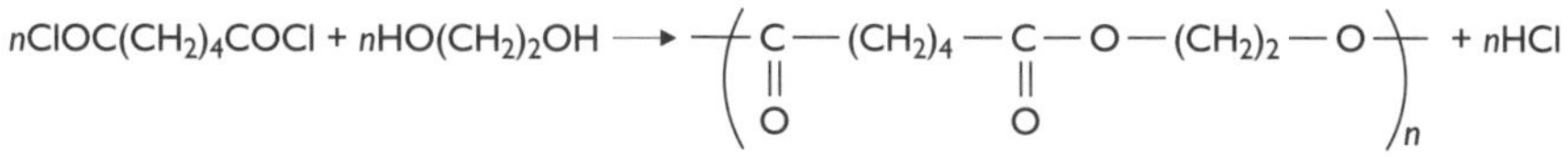

$$nClOC(CH_2)_4COCl + nHO(CH_2)_2OH \longrightarrow \left(\overset{\displaystyle}{\underset{\displaystyle O}{C}} - (CH_2)_4 - \overset{\displaystyle}{\underset{\displaystyle O}{C}} - O - (CH_2)_2 - O \right)_n + nHCl$$

Reaction with ammonia

With concentrated ammonia solution, an amide is rapidly formed. For example, with ethanoyl chloride the product is ethanamide.

$$CH_3COCl + 2NH_3 \longrightarrow CH_3CONH_2 + NH_4Cl$$

Reaction with amines

In this reaction, a substituted amide is produced, which contains the –CONH– peptide link — for example:

$$CH_3COCl + C_2H_5NH_2 \longrightarrow CH_3CONHC_2H_5 + HCl$$

A **polyamide** can be produced by reacting molecules containing two acid chloride groups with molecules containing two amine groups.

$$nClOC(CH_2)_4COCl + nH_2N(CH_2)_2NH_2 \longrightarrow \left(\overset{\displaystyle}{\underset{\displaystyle O}{C}} - (CH_2)_4 - \overset{\displaystyle}{\underset{\displaystyle O}{\underset{\displaystyle H}{C}}} - \overset{\displaystyle}{\underset{\displaystyle}{N}} - (CH_2)_2 - \overset{\displaystyle}{\underset{\displaystyle H}{N}} \right)_n + nHCl$$

Note: carboxylic acids do not react with amines to form substituted amides — they react to form salts.

Esters

Esters contain the group:

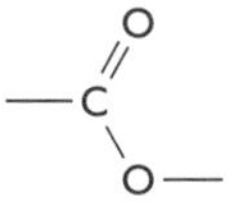

Reactions

Reaction with alkalis

When an ester is heated under reflux with an aqueous solution of an alkali such as sodium hydroxide, the ester is hydrolysed to an alcohol and the salt of a carboxylic acid in an *irreversible* reaction.

$$CH_3COOCH_3 + NaOH \longrightarrow CH_3OH + CH_3COONa$$
methyl ethanoate   methanol   sodium ethanoate

Fats are esters of propan-1,2,3-triol (glycerol) and large carboxylic acids such as stearic acid, $C_{17}H_{35}COOH$. When heated under reflux with aqueous sodium hydroxide, sodium stearate, $C_{17}H_{35}COONa$, is produced. This is a soap and the reaction is called **saponification**.

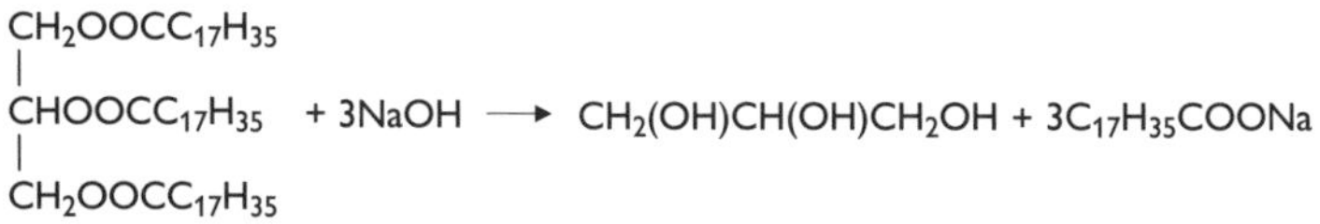

$$
\begin{array}{l}
CH_2OOCC_{17}H_{35} \\
| \\
CHOOCC_{17}H_{35} \quad + 3NaOH \longrightarrow CH_2(OH)CH(OH)CH_2OH + 3C_{17}H_{35}COONa \\
| \\
CH_2OOCC_{17}H_{35}
\end{array}
$$

Reaction with acids

Esters are *reversibly* hydrolysed when heated under reflux with an aqueous solution of a strong acid, which acts as a catalyst. Ethyl ethanoate is hydrolysed to ethanoic acid and ethanol.

$$CH_3COOC_2H_5 + H_2O \rightleftharpoons CH_3COOH + C_2H_5OH$$

Carbonyl compounds

Carbonyl compounds contain the C=O group. There are two types of carbonyl compound.

- **Aldehydes** have a hydrogen atom on the carbonyl carbon and so have a –CHO group. Examples include methanal (HCHO), ethanal (CH_3CHO) and propanal (CH_3CH_2CHO).
- **Ketones** have *two* alkyl groups attached to the carbonyl carbon atom. Examples include propanone (CH_3COCH_3) and butanone ($CH_3COCH_2CH_3$).

Preparation
Aldehydes

An aldehyde is prepared by oxidising a *primary* alcohol and distilling off the aldehyde as it is produced. For example, a mixture of potassium dichromate(VI) and sulphuric acid is added to hot ethanol and the ethanal distils off.

$$CH_3CH_2OH + [O] \longrightarrow CH_3CHO + H_2O$$

Ketones

Ketones are prepared by heating a *secondary* alcohol under reflux with an oxidising agent, such as a solution of potassium dichromate(VI) and sulphuric acid.

$$CH_3CH(OH)CH_3 + [O] \longrightarrow CH_3COCH_3 + H_2O$$

Reactions of aldehydes and ketones

The carbon atom is $\delta+$. Therefore, carbonyl compounds react with nucleophiles.

Reaction with 2,4-dinitrophenylhydrazine

Both aldehydes and ketones form an orange-yellow precipitate with a solution of 2,4-dinitrophenylhydrazine.

$$CH_3CHO + H_2NNHC_6H_3(NO_2)_2 \longrightarrow CH_3CH=NNHC_6H_3(NO_2)_2 + H_2O$$

This is an example of a **nucleophilic substitution** reaction. It is used as a test for aldehydes and ketones.

Reaction with hydrogen cyanide

Although the reactant is hydrogen cyanide, potassium cyanide in a buffer solution at pH 8 is added to the carbonyl compound. This is necessary because the attack is by the nucleophile CN^-, followed by the addition of H^+. For the reaction with ethanal, the organic product is 2-hydroxypropanenitrile.

$$CH_3CHO + HCN \longrightarrow CH_3CH(OH)CN$$

For the reaction with propanone, the organic product is 2-hydroxy-2-methylpropane-nitrile.

$$CH_3COCH_3 + HCN \longrightarrow CH_3C(CN)(OH)CH_3$$

The overall reactions are examples of nucleophilic addition.

Reduction

Aldehydes and ketones can be reduced by lithium aluminium hydride ($LiAlH_4$) in dry ether, or by an aqueous solution of sodium borohydride ($NaBH_4$).

$$CH_3COCH_3 + 2[H] \longrightarrow CH_3CH(OH)CH_3$$

This is another example of a nucleophilic addition reaction.

Reaction with Grignard reagents

Aldehydes and ketones react with Grignard reagents by nucleophilic addition, to form alcohols (see pages 58–59).

Reactions of aldehydes only

Aldehydes contain the –CHO group, which can be oxidised to –COOH or to the –COO⁻ ion.

Reaction with Fehling's solution

When an aldehyde is warmed with Fehling's solution, a red precipitate of copper(I) oxide is formed from the blue solution. The aldehyde is oxidised to a carboxylate ion.

$$CH_3CHO + [O] + OH^- \longrightarrow CH_3COO^- + H_2O$$

Reaction with ammoniacal silver nitrate

When an aldehyde is added to a solution of silver nitrate in dilute ammonia and warmed, a silver mirror is formed. Ethanal is oxidised to the ethanoate ion.

$$CH_3CHO + [O] + OH^- \longrightarrow CH_3COO^- + H_2O$$

These two reactions are used to distinguish an aldehyde from a ketone.

Iodoform reaction of ethanal and methyl ketones

Compounds with a –COCH₃ group undergo this reaction, forming a pale yellow precipitate of iodoform, CHI_3.

$$CH_3CHO + 3I_2 + 4NaOH \longrightarrow CHI_3 + 3NaI + HCOONa + 3H_2O$$
$$CH_3COR + 3I_2 + 4NaOH \longrightarrow CHI_3 + 3NaI + RCOONa + 3H_2O$$

Note: ethanol (CH_3CH_2OH) and secondary alcohols containing the $CH_3CH(OH)$ group also undergo this reaction. They are initially oxidised to ethanal and methyl ketones respectively, which react further to produce iodoform.

Primary amines

Primary amines contain the –NH₂ group, for example ethylamine, $C_2H_5NH_2$.

Reactions

Reaction with acids

Amines are weak bases, just like ammonia, and so react with both strong and weak acids to form salts. With a strong acid, such as hydrochloric acid, the product is ethylammonium chloride.

$$C_2H_5NH_2 + HCl \longrightarrow C_2H_5NH_3^+Cl^-$$

This is similar to the reaction of ammonia with hydrochloric acid.

$$NH_3 + HCl \longrightarrow NH_4^+Cl^-$$

With a weak acid, such as ethanoic acid, the product is ethylammonium ethanoate.

$$C_2H_5NH_2 + CH_3COOH \longrightarrow C_2H_5NH_3{}^+CH_3COO^-$$

Reaction with acid chlorides
See page 61.

Nitriles
Nitriles contain the –CN group. The stem of their names is determined by the total number of carbon atoms in the chain, including the carbon of the CN group.

Reactions
Hydrolysis
When heated under reflux with an acid or with an alkali, followed by acidification, a carboxylic acid is formed.

$$RCN + H^+ + 2H_2O \longrightarrow RCOOH + NH_4{}^+$$

Hydroxynitriles, such as $CH_3CH(OH)CN$, also undergo this reaction. The organic product is 2-hydroxypropanoic acid (lactic acid).

$$CH_3CH(OH)CN + H^+ + 2H_2O \longrightarrow CH_3CH(OH)COOH + NH_4{}^+$$

Reduction
Lithium aluminium hydride, $LiAlH_4$, in dry ether reduces nitriles to a primary amines. For example:

$$CH_3CN + 4[H] \longrightarrow CH_3CH_2NH_2$$

Amides
Amides contain the –$CONH_2$ group.

Reactions
Reaction with phosphorus(V) oxide
When warmed, the amide is dehydrated to a nitrile. For example:

$$CH_3CONH_2 - H_2O \longrightarrow CH_3CN$$

The product is ethanenitrile.

Hofmann degradation reaction
This reaction reduces the carbon chain length by one carbon atom. The amide is mixed with liquid bromine. Concentrated sodium hydroxide is added and the mixture warmed. The amine distils off. An example is:

$$CH_3CONH_2 \longrightarrow CH_3NH_2$$

Amino acids
Amino acids contain both –NH_2 and –COOH groups. Most contain a chiral centre. For example, 2-aminopropanoic acid, $CH_3CH(NH_2)COOH$, has two optical isomers.

Mirror

Amino acids are water-soluble solids. The reason for this is that the acidic –COOH group protonates the basic –NH_2 group, forming a **zwitterion** which has a positive charge on one end and a negative charge on the other.

$$NH_2CH_2COOH \rightleftharpoons {}^+NH_3CH_2COO^-$$

The ion–ion attractions result in the substance being a solid. The ion–dipole attractions with the $\delta+$ H and $\delta-$ O atoms in the water cause its solubility.

Note: protein molecules are long chains of different amino acids joined by peptide links.

Reactions
Reaction with acids
The –NH_2 group becomes protonated.

$$NH_2CH_2COOH + H^+ \longrightarrow {}^+NH_3CH_2COOH$$

Reaction with bases
The –COOH protonates the base.

$$NH_2CH_2COOH + OH^- \longrightarrow NH_2CH_2COO^- + H_2O$$

Summary
Grignard reagents

C_2H_5MgBr
- $+ CO_2 \longrightarrow C_2H_5COOH$
- $+ HCHO \longrightarrow C_2H_5CH_2OH$
- $+ CH_3CHO \longrightarrow C_2H_5CH(OH)CH_3$
- $+ CH_3COCH_3 \longrightarrow C_2H_5C(CH_3)(OH)CH_3$

Carboxylic acids

CH_3COOH
- $+ OH^-(aq) \longrightarrow CH_3COO^-(aq) + H_2O(l)$
- $+ NaHCO_3 \longrightarrow CH_3COONa + CO_2 + H_2O$
- $+ C_2H_5OH \longrightarrow CH_3COOC_2H_5 + H_2O$
- $+ PCl_5 \longrightarrow CH_3COCl + POCl_3 + HCl$
- $+ LiAlH_4 \longrightarrow CH_3CH_2OH$

Acid chlorides

CH_3COCl
- $+ H_2O \longrightarrow CH_3COOH + HCl$
- $+ C_2H_5OH \longrightarrow CH_3COOC_2H_5 + HCl$
- $+ NH_3 \longrightarrow CH_3CONH_2 + NH_4Cl$
- $+ C_2H_5NH_2 \longrightarrow CH_3CONHC_2H_5 + HCl$

Esters

$CH_3COOC_2H_5$ + $OH^-(aq)$ → $CH_3COO^-(aq) + C_2H_5OH$

$CH_3COOC_2H_5$ + $H^+(aq)$ → $CH_3COOH + C_2H_5OH$

Aldehydes and ketones

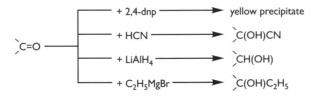

$>C=O$ + 2,4-dnp → yellow precipitate

$>C=O$ + HCN → $>C(OH)CN$

$>C=O$ + $LiAlH_4$ → $>CH(OH)$

$>C=O$ + C_2H_5MgBr → $>C(OH)C_2H_5$

Aldehydes only

CH_3CHO + Fehling's → red ppt + CH_3COO^-

CH_3CHO + $AgNO_3/NH_3$ → silver mirror + CH_3COO^-

Amines

$C_2H_5NH_2$ + $H^+(aq)$ → $C_2H_5NH_3^+$

$C_2H_5NH_2$ + CH_3COCl → $CH_3CONHC_2H_5 + HCl$

Nitriles

CH_3CN + $H^+(aq)$ → $CH_3COOH + NH_4^+(aq)$

CH_3CN + $LiAlH_4$ → $CH_3CH_2NH_2$

Amides

CH_3CONH_2 + P_2O_5 → $CH_3CN + H_2O$

CH_3CONH_2 + $Br_2/NaOH$ → CH_3NH_2

Amino acids

NH_2CH_2COOH + $H^+(aq)$ → $^+NH_3CH_2COOH$

NH_2CH_2COOH + $OH^-(aq)$ → $NH_2CH_2COO^- + H_2O$

Questions
&
Answers

The following questions are drawn from recent unit tests. Do not treat the answers as model answers or as rubber-stamp responses to be reproduced without thought. The most important reason for studying chemistry is to *understand* it, not merely to repeat it parrot-fashion — you have to do more than simply aim for a good grade.

In some instances, the difference between an A-grade response and a C-grade response has been suggested. This is not always possible, since many of the questions are rather short and do not require extended writing.

I do not suggest that this section covers all the possible questions that could be asked on Unit Test 4 — examiners are more resourceful than that. However, there are examples of questions on each topic of Unit 4.

Examiner's comments

Candidate responses to long-answer questions are followed by examiner's comments, preceded by the icon 🄴. They are interspersed in the answers and indicate where credit is due. They also point out common errors that lower-grade answers are prone to show.

Unit Test 4, January 2002 and June 2002

Question 1

(a) (i) Write an equation for the reaction between magnesium oxide and dilute sulphuric acid, including the state symbols. (2 marks)

(ii) Describe what you would see during this reaction. (2 marks)

(b) (i) Write an equation for the reaction between phosphorus(V) oxide and aqueous sodium hydroxide solution. (2 marks)

(ii) With the aid of *two* equations, show how aluminium hydroxide exhibits amphoteric character. (3 marks)

(c) With reference to the reactions in (a) and (b), describe the variation in the metallic character of the *elements* across period 3 of the periodic table (sodium to argon). (2 marks)

(d) Suggest, with reasoning, the acid–base character of indium(III) oxide, In_2O_3. Indium is the fourth element down group 3 of the periodic table. (2 marks)

Total: 13 marks

Answer to Question 1

(a) (i) $MgO(s) + H_2SO_4(aq) \longrightarrow MgSO_4(aq) + H_2O(l)$ ✓✓

There is 1 mark for the balanced equation and 1 mark for the state symbols. The only insoluble sulphates are those of barium, strontium and lead(II). C-grade candidates often think that, if state symbols are asked for in inorganic chemistry, there must be a precipitate or gas formed.

(ii) The white solid ✓ reacts to form a colourless solution ✓.

If you are asked to describe what you would see in a reaction, you need to say what the reaction mixture looks like both *before* and *after* the reaction. Many C-grade candidates fail to give the initial colour or physical state.

(b) (i) $P_4O_{10} + 12NaOH \longrightarrow 4Na_3PO_4 + 6H_2O$ ✓✓

There is 1 mark for the correct formulae of species on both sides of the equation and 1 mark for balancing it. A correct equation starting with P_2O_5 (which is the one above halved) would also score full marks.

(ii) • $Al(OH)_3 + 3H^+ \longrightarrow Al^{3+} + 3H_2O$ ✓
$Al(OH)_3 + 3OH^- \longrightarrow [Al(OH)_6]^{3-}$ ✓
• $Al(OH)_3 + 3HCl \longrightarrow AlCl_3 + 3H_2O$ ✓
$Al(OH)_3 + 3NaOH \longrightarrow Na_3Al(OH)_6$ ✓
Amphoteric means a substance that reacts with both acids and alkalis ✓.

🖉 Two alternative sets of equations are given. There is 1 mark for an equation with $Al(OH)_3$ and an acid (or H^+) on the left-hand side and 1 mark for an equation with $Al(OH)_3$ and an alkali (or OH^-) on the left-hand side. The third mark is for an explanation of amphoteric in words or by having H^+ and OH^- on the left in two equations.

(c) The trend is that the elements go from being metals to non-metals on moving from left to right across the period ✓. This is shown by the fact that magnesium oxide is a base (a typical metal oxide property), aluminium oxide is amphoteric and phosphorus(V) oxide is acidic (a typical non-metal oxide property) ✓.

🖉 You *must* state the trend, making it clear that you are describing the trend from left to right across the period, and then justify the trend in terms of the chemical properties of the oxides mentioned in **(a)** and **(b)**. C-grade candidates often miss out the justification or use other data, such as the properties of the elements themselves. You must read the question carefully.

(d) Indium(III) oxide would be basic ✓. As a group is descended, the elements become more metallic and therefore their oxides are more basic. Indium is two places below aluminium and so indium(III) oxide will be more basic than aluminium oxide ✓.

🖉 You are not expected to *know* anything about indium. You should be able to deduce the property based on your knowledge of the periodic table.

■ ■ ■

Question 2

(a) The formation of magnesium chloride from magnesium and chlorine can be represented by the following Born–Haber cycle:

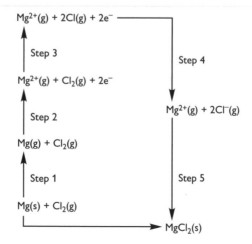

(i) Define the following terms:
  - lattice energy (3 marks)
  - enthalpy of atomisation (2 marks)

(ii) Which step in the cycle above represents the enthalpy of atomisation of magnesium? (1 mark)

(iii) Use the data below to calculate the first electron affinity of chlorine. (2 marks)

Enthalpy change	Value of the enthalpy change/kJ mol^{-1}
Enthalpy of atomisation of magnesium	+150
First ionisation energy of magnesium	+736
Second ionisation energy of magnesium	+1450
Enthalpy of formation of magnesium chloride	−642
Enthalpy of atomisation of chlorine	+121
Lattice energy of magnesium chloride	−2493

(b) Hydrogen gas reacts with sodium metal to form an ionic solid, NaH, which contains sodium cations. Draw a Born–Haber cycle that could be used to determine the electron affinity of hydrogen. (3 marks)

Total: 11 marks

Answer to Question 2

(a) (i) Lattice energy is the exothermic heat change ✓ when the gaseous ions ✓ come together to form 1 mol of solid ✓.

Enthalpy of atomisation is the heat energy (or enthalpy) change for the formation of 1 mol of gaseous atoms ✓ from the element in its standard state ✓.

🖉 The lattice energy must be defined in the exothermic direction. In defining enthalpy of atomisation, C-grade candidates often fail to state that the element must be in its standard state — for instance, solid iodine or gaseous chlorine.

(ii) Step 1 ✓

(iii) ΔH_f of $MgCl_2 = \Delta H_{step\,1} + \Delta H_{step\,2} + \Delta H_{step\,3} + \Delta H_{step\,4} + \Delta H_{step\,5}$
$-642 = +150 + (736 + 1450) + 2 \times (+121) + 2 \times$ electron affinity $+ (-2493)$ ✓
$2 \times$ electron affinity $= 2493 - 642 - 150 - 2186 - 242 = -727$

electron affinity of chlorine $= \dfrac{-727}{2} = -364$ kJ mol^{-1} ✓

🖉 C-grade candidates may fail to realise that step 3 is for the formation of 2 mol of chlorine atoms, and has a value of 2×121 kJ, and that step 4 requires the electron affinity of chlorine to be doubled.

(b)

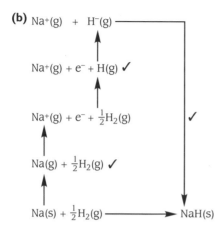

Na$^+$(g) + H$^-$(g) ——————

Na$^+$(g) + e$^-$ + H(g) ✓

Na$^+$(g) + e$^-$ + $\frac{1}{2}$H$_2$(g)   ✓

Na(g) + $\frac{1}{2}$H$_2$(g) ✓

Na(s) + $\frac{1}{2}$H$_2$(g) ——————→ NaH(s)

There is 1 mark for the steps from Na(s) to Na$^+$(g), 1 mark for the steps from $\frac{1}{2}$H$_2$(g) to H$^-$(g) and 1 mark for a complete cycle. The question tells you that sodium cations are present in the hydride. Therefore, there must be hydrogen *anions*, H$^-$, present. C-grade candidates often miss this and include H$^+$ in their Born–Haber cycles, therefore failing to score any marks.

■ ■ ■

Question 3

(a) (i) **Give the structural formula of a nitrile, C$_4$H$_7$N, that has an unbranched chain.** (1 mark)

(ii) **Primary amines can be made by reducing nitriles. Suggest a reagent that could be used for this purpose.** (1 mark)

(iii) **Draw the structural formula of the amine produced by reducing the nitrile in (a)(i).** (1 mark)

(b) **Draw the structure of an isomer of C$_4$H$_{11}$N that has a chiral centre in the molecule. Identify the chiral centre.** (2 marks)

(c) (i) **What feature of the amine molecule makes it both a base and a nucleophile?** (1 mark)

(ii) **By writing an equation, given an example of an amine acting as a base.** (1 mark)

(d) **Ethanoyl chloride, CH$_3$COCl, reacts with both amines and alcohols.**

(i) **Give the name of the type of compound produced when ethanoyl chloride reacts with ethylamine, C$_2$H$_5$NH$_2$.** (1 mark)

(ii) **State *one* advantage of reacting ethanoyl chloride with ethanol to make an ester, rather than reacting ethanoic acid with ethanol.** (1 mark)

(e) **Ethanoyl chloride can be made from ethanoic acid. Suggest a suitable reagent for this conversion.** (1 mark)

(f) **Suggest how chloromethane can be converted into ethanoic acid via a Grignard reagent. (Details of the experimental apparatus are not required.)** (4 marks)

Total: 14 marks

Answer to Question 3

(a) (i) $CH_3CH_2CH_2C{\equiv}N$ ✓

✏ If the *full* structural formula had been asked for, you would have to show *all* the atoms and bonds.

(ii) Lithium aluminium hydride (lithium tetrahydridoaluminate(III)), $LiAlH_4$ ✓

✏ Either the name or the formula is acceptable. Other reducing agents, such as sodium borohydride, $NaBH_4$, or hydrogen gas with a nickel or platinum catalyst, will reduce nitriles.

(iii)

✏ This time you are asked to *draw* the structural formula, so a full diagram is necessary.

(b)

✏ Remember that four different groups attached to a carbon atom can *identify* a chiral centre. However, this is not the *definition* of a chiral centre. A chiral centre causes the molecule to have a non-superimposable mirror image.

(c) (i) The lone pair of electrons on the nitrogen atom ✓

(ii) • $C_4H_9NH_2 + H^+ \longrightarrow C_4H_9NH_3^+$ ✓

• $C_4H_9NH_2 + HCl \longrightarrow C_4H_9NH_3^+Cl^-$ ✓

✏ Two alternative answers to part (ii) are given.

(d) (i) A (substituted) amide ✓

(ii) As the reaction of an acid chloride with an alcohol is not reversible, unlike that of an acid with an alcohol, the yield using the acid chloride will be greater ✓.

✏ You must *compare* the reactions of the acid chloride and the acid with ethanol. C-grade candidates often fail to mention both substances.

(e) Phosphorus(V) chloride, PCl_5 ✓

(f) Make a Grignard reagent by reacting the chloromethane with magnesium ✓ in dry ether ✓ to produce CH_3MgCl. Then react this with solid carbon dioxide ✓ and finally hydrolyse the adduct with dilute hydrochloric acid ✓.

✏ C-grade candidates often fail to say that hydrolysis of the product of the reaction between a Grignard reagent and carbon dioxide or carbonyl compounds is necessary.

■ ■ ■

Question 4

Consider the following reaction scheme, starting from propanone:

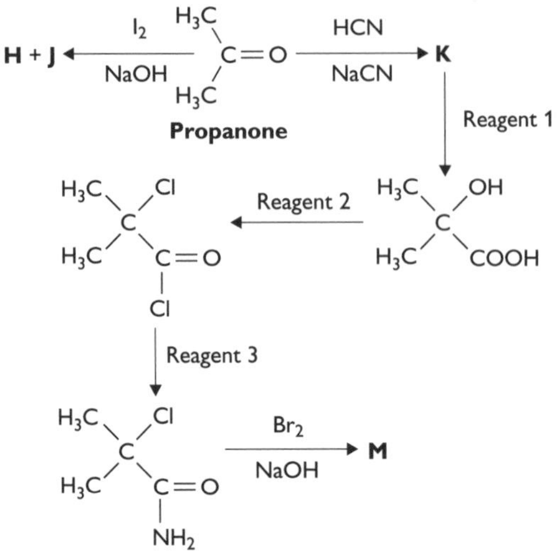

(a) Give the structural formula of compounds H, J, K and M.   (4 marks)
(b) Identify reagent 1, reagent 2 and reagent 3.   (3 marks)
(c) Compounds produced when glucose, $C_6H_{12}O_6$, is metabolised include:
   - 2,3-dihydroxypropanal, $CH_2(OH)CH(OH)CHO$
   - 2-oxopropanoic acid, $CH_3COCOOH$
   - 2-hydroxypropanoic acid, $CH_3CH(OH)COOH$
   (i) Draw the full structural formula for 2,3-dihydroxypropanal.   (1 mark)
   (ii) Suggest which two of these compounds would give a positive test with
        2,4-dinitrophenylhydrazine solution. State what you would see in a
        positive result.   (3 marks)
   (iii) Describe a test that would enable you to distinguish between the two
        compounds identified in (ii).   (2 marks)

                                                                    Total: 13 marks

Answer to Question 4

(a) H is CHI_3 ✓
    J is CH_3COONa ✓

    K is $H_3C-\overset{\displaystyle CH_3}{\underset{\displaystyle CN}{C}}-OH$ or $CH_3C(OH)(CN)CH_3$ ✓

    M is $H_3C-\overset{\displaystyle CH_3}{\underset{\displaystyle OH}{C}}-NH_2$ or $CH_3C(OH)(NH_2)CH_3$ ✓

📝 C-grade answers often give the Hofmann degradation reaction but omit the hydrolysis of the C–Cl bond. With molecules that have two side chains, it is easier to draw the structure. If you use the shorthand version, you *must* put brackets around the groups such as OH and NH_2 on the side chain, as shown.

(b) Reagent 1 is a strong acid, such as dilute hydrochloric acid ✓.
Reagent 2 is phosphorus(V) chloride ✓.
Reagent 3 is ammonia solution ✓.

📝 The formulae would also be acceptable.

(c) (i)

(ii) The two compounds that give a positive test with 2,4-dinitrophenylhydrazine are 2,3-dihydroxypropanal ✓ and 2-oxopropanoic acid ✓. The result is an orange precipitate ✓.

(iii) • Identify the aldehyde by warming with Fehling's solution ✓. 2,3-dihydroxy-propanal gives a red precipitate, whereas 2-oxopropanoic acid does not ✓.
  • Identify the aldehyde by adding ammoniacal silver nitrate ✓. 2,3-dihydroxy-propanal gives a silver mirror, whereas 2-oxopropanoic acid does not ✓.
  • Identify the acid by adding sodium carbonate (or sodium hydrogen carbonate) ✓. 2-oxopropanoic acid fizzes, giving off carbon dioxide, whereas 2,3-dihydroxypropanal does not ✓.
  • Identify which is an aldehyde or a primary or secondary alcohol by warming with potassium dichromate(VI) in sulphuric acid solution ✓. 2,3-dihydroxy-propanal turns the orange solution green, whereas 2-oxopropanoic acid does not ✓.

📝 Alternative answers are given. C-grade candidates often fail to say what both substances do in the test. The negative point, that one of the compounds being tested does not react, is vital. Phosphorus(V) chloride cannot be used for the test because both alcohols and acids give off steamy fumes of hydrogen chloride.

■ ■ ■

Question 5

(a) Methane reacts with steam in a reversible reaction. In industry, this reaction, carried out at a pressure of 30 atm, is used to produce hydrogen for the manufacture of ammonia.

$$CH_4(g) + H_2O(g) \rightleftharpoons CO(g) + 3H_2(g) \qquad \Delta H = +210 \text{ kJ mol}^{-1}$$

(i) Define the term *partial pressure*, as applied to a gas mixture. (1 mark)
(ii) Write an expression for the equilibrium constant, K_p, for this reaction. (1 mark)
(iii) State and explain the effect of increasing the total pressure on the position of this equilibrium. (2 marks)

(b) State the effect of the following on the value of K_p for this equilibrium:
  (i) increasing the total pressure (1 mark)
  (ii) increasing the temperature (1 mark)
  (iii) adding a catalyst (1 mark)
(c) Methane, CH_4, constantly leaks from the earth's crust. This is not noticeable on land but at the bottom of a cold sea, such as off the Canadian coast, the methane is trapped in a solid cage of water molecules.

$$CH_4(g) + 6H_2O(s) \rightleftharpoons [CH_4(H_2O)_6](s)$$
Methane hydrate

At –29 °C, the equilibrium partial pressure of methane is 101.3 kPa.
  (i) Write an expression for K_p for this equilibrium. (1 mark)
  (ii) Deduce the value of K_p at –29 °C, stating its units. (1 mark)
  (iii) At 0 °C, the equilibrium partial pressure of methane rises to 2600 kPa. What does this tell you about the effect of temperature change on the position of equilibrium and about the enthalpy change for this reaction? (2 marks)
  (iv) Some people have suggested collecting the methane hydrate from the bottom of the sea and allowing it to warm up to 0 °C on board ship. Comment on whether this would be a useful method for collecting methane. (1 mark)

Total: 12 marks

Answer to Question 5

(a) (i) • The pressure the gas would exert if it were on its own in the same volume and at the same temperature ✓
  • The fraction of the total pressure exerted by the gas ✓
  • The mole fraction of the gas multiplied by the total pressure ✓

✎ Any one of the three alternative answers given is acceptable.

(ii) $K_p = \dfrac{p(CO)p(H_2)^3}{p(CH_4)p(H_2O)}$ ✓

✎ The expression must be completely correct to gain the mark. You must *not* use square brackets in expressions for K_p. The partial pressure of water is included as it is a gas under these conditions.

(iii) Because there are fewer gas molecules on the left of the equation than on the right ✓, the position of equilibrium shifts to the left ✓ when the pressure is increased.

(b) (i) Increasing the total pressure has no effect ✓ on the value of K_p.
  (ii) Increasing the temperature causes K_p to increase ✓ (as the reaction is endothermic left to right).
  (iii) Adding a catalyst has no effect ✓.

✎ The only factor that alters the value of K_p for a given reaction is a change in temperature.

(c) (i) $K_p = \dfrac{1}{p(CH_4)}$ ✓

　(ii) $K_p = \dfrac{1}{101.3} = 0.00987 \text{ kPa}^{-1}$ ✓

　(iii) At the higher temperature, there is a higher pressure of methane, so the equilibrium position is further to the left ✓. Therefore, the reaction must be exothermic left to right (or endothermic right to left)✓.

🖉 You must not say that the reaction is exothermic (or endothermic) without saying *in which direction*.

　(iv) This should be a good method as long as the quantities of methane hydrate are large enough to make it economically worthwhile ✓.

■ ■ ■

Question 6

(a) A weak acid, represented by **HA**, dissociates in water according to the equation:

$$HA(aq) + H_2O(l) \rightleftharpoons H_3O^+(aq) + A^-(aq)$$

Write an expression for the acid dissociation constant, K_a, for **HA**.　　　　(1 mark)

(b) 25 cm³ of 1.00 mol dm⁻³ aqueous **HA** was titrated with 1.00 mol dm⁻³ aqueous sodium hydroxide. The pH was measured throughout. The titration curve is shown below:

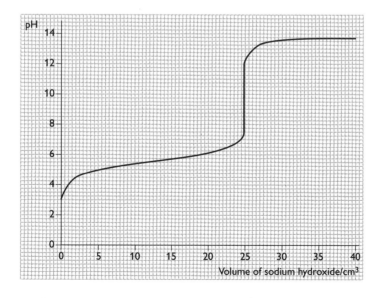

Use the titration curve to find:

(i)　the value of the pH at the end point of the titration　　　　(1 mark)

(ii)　the pH of an aqueous solution of the salt **NaA**　　　　(1 mark)

(iii)　the value of pK_a for the acid **HA** and, hence, the value of K_a　　　　(2 marks)

(c) **Some of the solutions formed during this titration act as buffers.**
  (i) **What is meant by the term** *buffer solution?* (2 marks)
  (ii) **Use the titration curve to find:**
      • **the range of pH values over which this mixture acts as a buffer**
      • **the pH of the most efficient buffer solution** (2 marks)
(d) **A different monobasic weak acid, HX, has a dissociation constant of**
  1.8×10^{-5} mol dm^{-3}. Calculate the pH of a 1.00 mol dm^{-3} aqueous
  solution of acid HX. (3 marks)

Total: 12 marks

Answer to Question 6

(a) $K_a = \dfrac{[H_3O^+][A^-]}{[HA]}$ ✓

🔁 $[H_2O]$ must not be included in the expression for K_a, and H^+ in place of H_3O^+ would not be acceptable.

(b) (i) The end point pH is 9.6 ✓.

🔁 The pH at the end point is the pH *halfway* up the vertical part of the graph, which goes from 7.2 to 12.0.

(ii) The pH of a solution of NaA is 9.6 ✓.

🔁 At the end point, all the acid has been neutralised and so the result is a solution of the salt NaA.

(iii) $pK_a = 5.5$ ✓
  $K_a = 10^{-5.5} = 3.2 \times 10^{-6}\,\text{mol dm}^{-3}$ ✓

🔁 When the acid is *half* neutralised, which is when 12.5 cm^3 of sodium hydroxide has been added, the value of $[HA] = [A^-]$. When substituted in the expression for K_a, these values cancel, so $K_a = [H_3O^+]$. Therefore, pK_a of the acid is equal to the pH at this halfway point.

(c) (i) A buffer solution resists changes in pH ✓, when small amounts of acid or base are added ✓.

🔁 Do not say that a buffer solution has a *constant* pH, as its pH changes very slightly when some acid or base is added.

(ii) The flattest part of the graph is where the solution will act as a buffer and has pH values between 4.8 and 6.1 ✓, but it will be the most efficient when there are equal amounts of weak acid and its salt, which is at a pH of 5.5 ✓.

🔁 A solution containing similar amounts of weak acid and its salt will act as a buffer. As a rough guide, a solution acts as a buffer if the ratio of weak acid to salt is between 4:1 and 1:4 which, in this example, is between 5.0 cm^3 and 20 cm^3 of sodium hydroxide added to the original 25 cm^3 of acid. When 5.0 cm^3 of sodium hydroxide has been added, 5.0 cm³ of acid solution has been used up, leaving 25 − 5 = 20 cm³, and 5 cm³ of salt solution has been produced, giving a ratio of acid to salt of 20:5 or 4:1. The pH value after 5.0 cm³ has been added is 4.8 and the value after 20 cm³ has been added is 6.1. It is at its most efficient when the acid has been half neutralised, which is when the ratio of weak acid to salt is 1:1. In this example, this occurs when 12.5 cm³ of sodium hydroxide has been added, and the pH at this point is 5.5.

(d) $K_a = \dfrac{[H_3O^+][X^-]}{[HX]} = 1.8 \times 10^{-5}\,\text{mol dm}^{-3}$

$[H_3O^+] = [X^-]$

$[HX] = 1.00\,\text{mol dm}^{-3}$

$[H_3O^+]^2 = K_a[HX]$ ✓

$[H_3O^+] = \sqrt{1.8 \times 10^{-5} \times 1.00} = 0.00424\,\text{mol dm}^{-3}$ ✓

$pH = -\log[H_3O^+] = -\log 0.00424 = 2.37$ ✓

Set 2

Unit Test 4, January 2003

Question 1

(a) Write equations to show the reactions of the following elements with oxygen:

    (i)   aluminium   (1 mark)

    (ii) phosphorus   (1 mark)

    (iii) silicon   (1 mark)

(b) Write equations to show the reactions of the following compounds with water:

    (i) $AlCl_3$ (1 mark)

    (ii) PCl_5 (1 mark)

    (iii) $SiCl_4$ (1 mark)

(c) Explain why silicon chloride, $SiCl_4$, reacts with water at room temperature, whereas carbon tetrachloride, CCl_4, does not.   (4 marks)

Total: 10 marks

Answer to Question 1

(a) (i) $4Al + 3O_2 \longrightarrow 2Al_2O_3$ ✓

    (ii) $P_4 + 5O_2 \longrightarrow P_4O_{10}$ ✓

e An equation starting with P rather than P_4, and then finishing with P_2O_5, would be allowed:

$$4P + 5O_2 \longrightarrow 2P_2O_5$$

    (iii) $Si + O_2 \longrightarrow SiO_2$ ✓

(b) (i) • $2AlCl_3 + 3H_2O \longrightarrow Al_2O_3 + 6HCl$ ✓

        • $AlCl_3 + 6H_2O \longrightarrow [Al(H_2O)_6]^{3+} + 3Cl^-$✓

e Two alternative answers are given. If a limited amount of water is added, the hydrogen chloride escapes and aluminium oxide is left. If there is excess water, the hydrogen chloride remains in solution and, because it is acidic, reacts with the basic aluminium hydroxide, forming hydrated aluminium cations and chloride anions.

    (ii) $PCl_5 + 4H_2O \longrightarrow H_3PO_4 + 5HCl$ ✓

    (iii) $SiCl_4 + 2H_2O \longrightarrow SiO_2 + 4HCl$ ✓

(c) The lone pair of electrons on the oxygen in the water ✓ forms a dative bond ✓ with the $3d$ orbital in the silicon atom ✓, releasing enough energy to break the Si–Cl bond. In carbon tetrachloride, the carbon atom does not have a similar ($2d$) orbital and the small carbon atom is completely surrounded by four large chlorine atoms, causing steric hindrance ✓.

■ ■ ■

Question 2

(a) Define the following terms:

    (i) pH   (1 mark)

    (ii) K_w (1 mark)

(b) Explain the meaning of the term *strong* as applied to an acid or base.   (1 mark)

(c) Calculate the pH of the following solutions:

    (i) HCl(aq) of concentration $0.200 \, \text{mol dm}^{-3}$ (1 mark)

    (ii) NaOH(aq) of concentration $0.800 \, \text{mol dm}^{-3}$

          ($K_w = 1.00 \times 10^{-14} \, \text{mol}^2 \, \text{dm}^{-6}$)   (2 marks)

(d) HA is a weak acid with a dissociation constant $K_a = 5.62 \times 10^{-5} \, \text{mol dm}^{-3}$.

    (i) Write an expression for the dissociation constant, K_a, of HA.   (1 mark)

    (ii) Calculate the pH of a $0.400 \, \text{mol dm}^{-3}$ solution of HA.   (3 marks)

(e) A buffer solution contains HA(aq) at a concentration of $0.300 \, \text{mol dm}^{-3}$ and its sodium salt, NaA, at a concentration of $0.600 \, \text{mol dm}^{-3}$. Calculate the pH of this buffer solution.   (3 marks)

Total: 13 marks

Answer to Question 2

(a) (i) $\text{pH} = -\log_{10}[\text{H}^+]$ ✓

🗭 A definition in words — 'minus the log to the base ten of the hydrogen ion concentration in mol dm^{-3}' — is also acceptable.

    (ii) $K_w = [\text{H}^+][\text{OH}^-]$ ✓

🗭 H_3O^+ in place of H^+ is acceptable.

(b) A strong acid or base is one that totally ionises in solution ✓.

(c) (i) $[\text{H}^+] = 0.200 \, \text{mol dm}^{-3}$

        $\text{pH} = -\log[\text{H}^+] = -\log(0.200) = 0.70$ ✓

🗭 Strong acids are totally ionised, so the $[\text{H}^+]$ equals the concentration of the acid given in the question.

    (ii) $[\text{OH}^-] = 0.800 \, \text{mol dm}^{-3}$

        $\text{pOH} = -\log[\text{OH}^-] = -\log(0.800) = 0.097$ ✓

        $\text{pH} = 14 - \text{pOH} = 14 - 0.097 = 13.90$ ✓

🗭 This could also be calculated as follows:

    $[\text{OH}^-] = 0.800 \, \text{mol dm}^{-3}$

    $[\text{H}^+] = \dfrac{1.00 \times 10^{-14}}{[\text{OH}^-]} = 1.25 \times 10^{-14} \, \text{mol dm}^{-3}$

    $\text{pH} = -\log[\text{H}^+] = -\log(1.25 \times 10^{-14}) = 13.90$

    For strong bases with *one* $-\text{OH}$ group per formula, the OH^- concentration equals the concentration of base, as given in the question. It is always sensible to give answers to pH questions to 2 decimal places.

(d) (i) $K_a = \dfrac{[H^+][A^-]}{[HA]}$ ✓

💡 H_3O^+ in place of H^+ is acceptable as the equation can be written producing either H^+ or H_3O^+.

(ii) $[H^+] = [A^-]$

$[HA] = 0.400 \, mol \, dm^{-3}$

$K_a = 5.62 \times 10^{-5} \, mol \, dm^{-3}$

$[H^+]^2 = K_a[HA]$ ✓

$[H^+] = \sqrt{5.62 \times 10^{-5} \times 0.400} = 0.00474 \, mol \, dm^{-3}$ ✓

$pH = -\log(0.00474) = 2.32$ ✓

(e) $[HA] = [\text{weak acid}] = 0.300 \, mol \, dm^{-3}$

$[A^-] = [\text{salt of weak acid}] = 0.600 \, mol \, dm^{-3}$ ✓

$[H^+] = \dfrac{K_a[HA]}{[A^-]} = 5.62 \times 10^{-5} \times \dfrac{0.300}{0.600} = 2.81 \times 10^{-5} \, mol \, dm^{-3}$ ✓

$pH = -\log(2.81 \times 10^{-5}) = 4.55$ ✓

■ ■ ■

Question 3

(a) Write equations to show the reactions of the amino acid alanine, **$CH_3CH(NH_2)COOH$**, with:

    (i) HCl   (1 mark)

    (ii) NaOH   (1 mark)

(b) Explain why alanine has a relatively high melting temperature (290 °C).   (2 marks)

(c) Alanine exists as two optical isomers.

    (i) Draw diagrams to show the structures of the two optical isomers.   (2 marks)

    (ii) Explain how separate, pure samples of these optical isomers can be distinguished from each other.   (2 marks)

(d) A mixture of isomeric alkenes is obtained when butan-2-ol is dehydrated.

    (i) Draw diagrams of these two *structural* isomers.   (2 marks)

    (ii) One of the above structural isomers can exist as two different stereoisomers. Draw diagrams to illustrate clearly these two stereoisomers. Name the type of isomerism.   (3 marks)

Total: 13 marks

Answer to Question 3

(a) (i) $CH_3CH(NH_2)COOH + HCl \longrightarrow CH_3CH(NH_3^+Cl^-)COOH$ ✓

    (ii) $CH_3CH(NH_2)COOH + NaOH \longrightarrow CH_3CH(NH_2)COO^-Na^+ + H_2O$ ✓

💡 The two functional groups react independently. The $-NH_2$ group reacts with acids, forming salts containing the $-NH_3^+$ group. The $-COOH$ group reacts with bases, forming the $-COO^-$ group.

(b) The acid group protonates the amino group and a zwitterion of formula $CH_3CH(NH_3^+)COO^-$ is formed ✓. There are strong forces between the positive charge on one zwitterion and the negative charge on another ion. Therefore, much energy is required to separate the ions and hence melting temperature is high ✓.

📝 You must make it clear that the ion–ion force is between *different* zwitterions.

(c) (i)

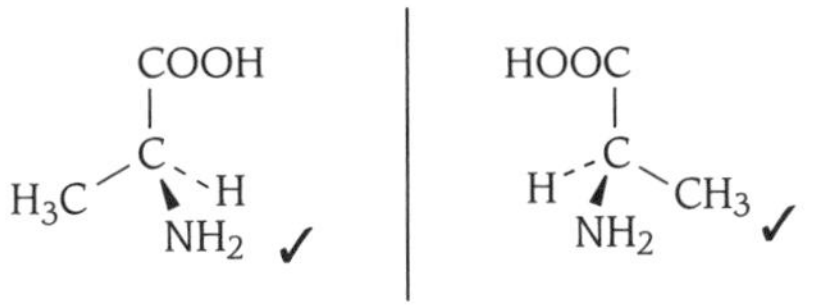

📝 You must draw the two optical isomers in three dimensions as mirror images of each other. Make sure that the bonds from the central carbon atom go to the correct atoms in the attached groups — for instance, to the carbon of the –COOH group.

(ii) The isomers rotate the plane of plane-polarised light ✓ in opposite directions ✓.

📝 C-grade candidates often use the incorrect terms 'bend' or 'deflect' rather than the correct term 'rotate'.

(d) (i)

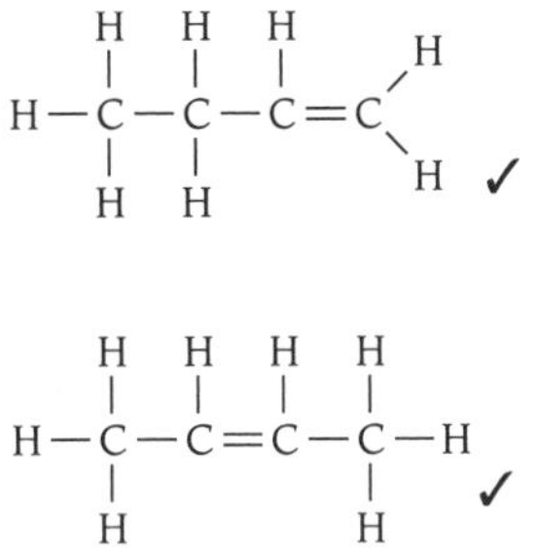

📝 $CH_3CH_2CH=CH_2$ and $CH_3CH=CHCH_3$ are not acceptable answers as the question asks for the formulae to be drawn.

(ii) The second of the structural isomers above shows geometric isomerism ✓.

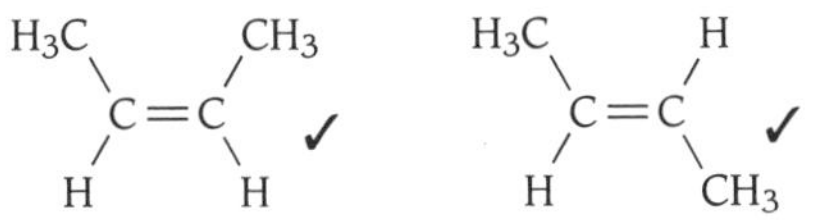

📝 Do not confuse structural isomerism with stereoisomerism. In **(i)**, the double bond is in different places in the carbon chain; in **(ii)** the CH_3 and H groups are arranged *cis* or *trans* across the double bond.

■ ■ ■

set **2**

Question 4

Consider the following equation:

$$2SO_2(g) + O_2(g) \rightleftharpoons 2SO_3$$

2.0 mol of SO_2 and 1.0 mol of O_2 were allowed to react in a vessel of volume 60 dm³. At equilibrium, 1.8 mol of SO_3 had formed and the pressure in the flask was 2 atm.

(a) (i) Write the expression for K_c for the reaction between SO_2 and O_2. (1 mark)
    (ii) Calculate the value of K_c, with units. (3 marks)

(b) The reaction between SO_2 and O_2 is exothermic. State the effect on the following, if the experiment is repeated at a higher temperature:
    (i) K_c (1 mark)
    (ii) the equilibrium position (1 mark)

(c) State the effect of a catalyst on:
    (i) K_c (1 mark)
    (ii) the equilibrium position (1 mark)

(d) (i) Write the expression for K_p for the reaction between SO_2 and O_2. (1 mark)
    (ii) Calculate the mole fractions of SO_2, O_2 and SO_3 at equilibrium. (2 marks)
    (iii) Calculate the partial pressures of SO_2, O_2 and SO_3 at equilibrium. (1 mark)
    (iv) Calculate the value of K_p, with units. (2 marks)

Total: 14 marks

Answer to Question 4

(a) (i) $K_c = \dfrac{[SO_3]_{eq}^2}{[SO_2]_{eq}^2[O_2]_{eq}}$ ✓

(ii) As 1.8 mole of SO_3 is formed, 1.8 mol of SO_2 and $\dfrac{1.8}{2} = 0.90$ mol of O_2 must have reacted.

	SO_2	O_2	SO_3
Moles at equilibrium	$2 - 1.8 = 0.20$	$1 - 0.90 = 0.10$	1.8
Concentration/ mol dm⁻³	$\dfrac{0.20}{60} = 0.00333$	$\dfrac{0.10}{60} = 0.00167$	$\dfrac{1.8}{60} = 0.030$ ✓

$$K_c = \frac{(0.030)^2}{(0.00333)^2(0.00167)} = 4.86 \times 10^4 \text{ ✓ mol}^{-1}\text{ dm}^3 \text{ ✓}$$

📝 It is essential to use equilibrium values and concentrations, not moles, in your calculation.

(b) (i) The value of K_c would decrease ✓.
    (ii) Therefore, the position of equilibrium would shift to the left ✓.

📝 The position of equilibrium moves in the *endothermic* direction when the temperature is increased.

(c) (i) A catalyst has no effect on the value of an equilibrium constant ✓.

(ii) It also has no effect on the equilibrium position ✓.

📝 Temperature is the only factor that alters the value of K. Changes in concentration and pressure alter the *position* of equilibrium but not the value of the constant.

(d) (i) $K_p = \dfrac{p(SO_3)^2}{p(SO_2)^2 p(O_2)}$ ✓

(ii) Using the moles at equilibrium calculated in (a)(ii):

The total moles are $0.2 + 0.1 + 1.8 = 2.1$ ✓

The mole fractions are:

$$SO_2 = \frac{0.2}{2.1} = 0.0952$$

$$O_2 = \frac{0.1}{2.1} = 0.0476$$

$$SO_3 = \frac{1.8}{2.1} = 0.857 ✓$$

(iii) Partial pressures are:

$SO_2 = 0.0952 \times 2 = 0.190\,\text{atm}$

$O_2 = 0.0476 \times 2 = 0.0952\,\text{atm}$

$SO_3 = 0.857 \times 2 = 1.71\,\text{atm}$ ✓

(iv) $K_p = \dfrac{(1.71)^2}{(0.190)^2(0.0952)} = 8.5 \times 10^2$ ✓ atm^{-1} ✓

■ ■ ■

Question 5

(a) Write the structural formulae and the names of the organic products obtained when ethanoyl chloride reacts with the following compounds:

(i) ammonia, NH_3 (2 marks)

(ii) methanol, CH_3OH (2 marks)

(b) Bromoethane reacts with magnesium to form the Grignard reagent CH_3CH_2MgBr. This Grignard reagent reacts with:

• **CO_2, followed by hydrochloric acid, to form compound A**

• **water, to form compound B**

• **methanal, followed by hydrochloric acid, to form compound C**

Compounds A and C react together, in the presence of a suitable catalyst, to form compound D.

(i) Write the structural formulae of compounds A, B and C. (3 marks)

(ii) Draw the full structural formula of compound D. (2 marks)

(iii) Give the names of compounds C and D. (2 marks)

(iv) Identify the catalyst for the reaction between compounds A and C. (1 mark)

Total: 12 marks

Answer to Question 5

(a) (i) CH_3CONH_2 ✓; ethanamide ✓
  (ii) CH_3COOCH_3 ✓; methyl ethanoate ✓

🖉 Acid chlorides react with ammonia to give amides and with alcohols to give esters. As the alcohol is methanol, the product is a *methyl* ester.

(b) (i) A is CH_3CH_2COOH ✓; B is CH_3CH_3 ✓; C is $CH_3CH_2CH_2OH$ ✓

🖉 Grignard reagents react with carbon dioxide to give carboxylic acids with one more carbon atom in the chain. They react with water to form alkanes with the same number of carbon atoms in the chain. They react with methanal to give primary alcohols with one more carbon atom in the chain.

(ii)

🖉 The full structural formula was asked for, so you must draw all the atoms and bonds.

(iii) C is propan-1-ol ✓; D is 1-propylpropanoate ✓

🖉 The stem is 'prop-' because there are three carbon atoms in the chain. The –OH group is on the first carbon atom, so the name ends in '-1-ol'. The acid A reacts with the alcohol C to form the ester D.

(iv) Concentrated sulphuric acid ✓

■ ■ ■

Question 6

(a) Define the term *lattice energy*. (3 marks)
(b) Construct a Born–Haber cycle for the formation of calcium chloride, $CaCl_2$. Use your cycle and the data below to calculate the lattice energy of calcium chloride. (5 marks)

	$\Delta H/kJ\,mol^{-1}$
Enthalpy of atomisation of calcium	+193
First ionisation energy of calcium	+590
Second ionisation energy of calcium	+1150
Enthalpy of formation of calcium chloride	−795
Enthalpy of atomisation of chlorine	+121
Electron affinity of chlorine	−370

(c) Explain why the lattice energy of magnesium fluoride, MgF_2, is more exothermic than that of calcium chloride. (3 marks)

(d) The theoretical and actual values of the lattice energy of magnesium fluoride are similar because magnesium fluoride is almost completely ionic. Explain why magnesium fluoride is almost completely ionic. (2 marks)

Total: 13 marks

Answer to Question 6

(a) The exothermic heat change ✓ when the gaseous ions ✓ form 1 mol of ionic solid ✓.

(b) Ca^{2+}(g) + 2Cl$^-$(g)

2 × (−370)

Ca^{2+}(g) + 2e$^-$ + 2Cl(g)

+1150

Ca$^+$(g) + e$^-$ + 2Cl(g)

LE

+590

Ca(g) + 2Cl(g)

+193

Ca(s) + 2Cl(g)

2 × (+121)

− 795

Ca(s) + Cl$_2$(g) ⟶ CaCl$_2$(s)

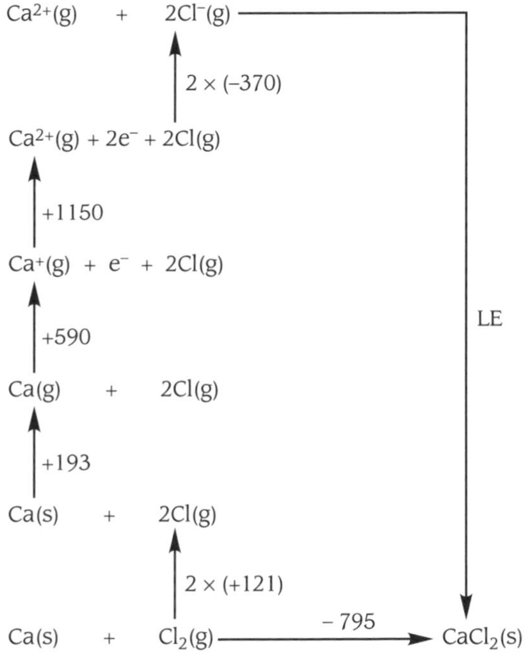

$-795 = 2 \times (+121) + 193 + 590 + 1150 + 2 \times (-370) + \text{LE}$

$\text{LE} = -795 - 242 - 193 - 590 - 1150 + 740 = -2230 \, \text{kJ mol}^{-1}$

There is 1 mark for each of the following:
- Born–Haber cycle with correct species
- all state symbols correct
- use of 2 × enthalpy of atomisation of chlorine
- use of 2 × electron affinity of chlorine
- the calculation, giving an answer of −2230 kJ mol^{-1}

The electrons need not be included in the cycle. You must show each change in the cycle separately. It is wise to put the enthalpy values beside the arrows. The enthalpy of atomisation is for the formation of *one* mole of atoms; therefore, +121 has to be multiplied by two. The electron affinity is for *one* mole of negative ion formed, so the value that must be used in this cycle is $2 \times (-370)$ kJ. C-grade candidates often forget to do this.

(c) The charges are the same in both compounds (both cations 2+ and both anions 1−). The lattice energy of magnesium fluoride is much more exothermic than that of calcium chloride because the radius of the Mg^{2+} ion is less than that of the Ca^{2+} ion ✓ and the radius of the F^- ion is less than that of the Cl^- ion ✓. Therefore, the sum of the ionic radii is less in MgF_2 than in $CaCl_2$ and this leads to a stronger force of attraction between the ions ✓.

The value of lattice energy depends *mainly* on two factors:
- the size of the charges on the cations and anions — the bigger the charges, the stronger is the force of attraction
- the sum of the radii of the cation and the anion — the smaller the sum, the stronger is the force

(d) The fluoride ion has a single charge and a very small radius ✓, so it is non-polarisable ✓.

C-grade candidates may state that the bond is 100% ionic because the theoretical and actual values are the same — the answer to a question that is often asked. You must read the question carefully and make sure that you answer the one asked!

periodic table

Period																			

Group

Key:
Molar mass/g mol⁻¹
Symbol
Atomic number

Group	1	2	3	4	5	6	7	0

Period 1

1
H
1

4
He
2

Period 2

7
Li
3

9
Be
4

11
B
5

12
C
6

14
N
7

16
O
8

19
F
9

20
Ne
10

Period 3

23
Na
11

24
Mg
12

27
Al
13

28
Si
14

31
P
15

32
S
16

35.5
Cl
17

40
Ar
18

Period 4

39
K
19

40
Ca
20

45
Sc
21

48
Ti
22

51
V
23

52
Cr
24

55
Mn
25

56
Fe
26

59
Co
27

59
Ni
28

63.5
Cu
29

65.4
Zn
30

70
Ga
31

73
Ge
32

75
As
33

79
Se
34

80
Br
35

84
Kr
36

Period 5

85
Rb
37

88
Sr
38

89
Y
39

91
Zr
40

93
Nb
41

96
Mo
42

99
Tc
43

101
Ru
44

103
Rh
45

106
Pd
46

108
Ag
47

112
Cd
48

115
In
49

119
Sn
50

122
Sb
51

128
Te
52

127
I
53

131
Xe
54

Period 6

133
Cs
55

137
Ba
56

139
La
57

178
Hf
72

181
Ta
73

184
W
74

186
Re
75

190
Os
76

192
Ir
77

195
Pt
78

197
Au
79

201
Hg
80

204
Tl
81

207
Pb
82

209
Bi
83

210
Po
84

210
At
85

222
Rn
86

Period 7

223
Fr
87

226
Ra
88

227
Ac
89

140
Ce
58

141
Pr
59

144
Nd
60

(147)
Pm
61

150
Sm
62

152
Eu
63

157
Gd
64

159
Tb
65

163
Dy
66

165
Ho
67

167
Er
68

169
Tm
69

173
Yb
70

175
Lu
71

232
Th
90

(231)
Pa
91

238
U
92

(237)
Np
93

(242)
Pu
94

(243)
Am
95

(247)
Cm
96

(245)
Bk
97

(251)
Cf
98

(254)
Es
99

(253)
Fm
100

(256)
Md
101

(254)
No
102

(257)
Lr
103